Wildlife Preservation

PHILIP STREET

Wildlife Preservation

Henry Regnery Company • Chicago

Contents

Wildlife Preservation

in one composite question: why do animals become rare and perhaps extinct; why should we attempt to avert this trend towards rarity and extinction; and if we do decide to make the attempt, how can we achieve success? This book attempts to answer these questions within a limited space. A complete, comprehensive book about fauna preservation would be either too long for most people to be able to spare the time to read it, or too expensive for them to be able to afford to buy it.

The logical first question to be answered in any survey concerned with the preservation of wildlife is what causes animals to become rare and in danger of extinction, and the answer is of course not simple. There are in fact many answers. Perhaps, however, the most important is concerned with the exploitation of commercially important species. Man does and must rely upon the animal kingdom for many of his essential requirements. Unfortunately he endangers the very species which are most important to him by over-exploitation, thus threatening to kill the geese that lay his golden eggs. Many examples will be found in subsequent chapters of commercially important species having been brought to the very brink of extinction by attempts to take a greater annual harvest than they are capable of supplying.

Besides the fur-bearing animals which are dealt with in Chapter 2, the most important animals which are faced with drastic reduction or even extinction by commercial exploitation are fish and whales. Fish of course make an important contribution to our food protein requirements, but since before the turn of the century, the gradual increase in the intensity of commercial fishing on all the major fishing grounds of the world has resulted in a progressive reduction in the number of available fish. This is reflected in the fact that today a much greater fishing effort, costing correspondingly more both in money and labour, is now needed to catch a given weight of any particular fish. The haddock, one of the most common fish in the North Sea, provides a good example of the drastic reduction of available stocks which has taken place. In 1906 the average daily catch of haddock landed by English steam trawlers fishing in the North Sea was 7.8 cwt., whereas thirty years later much larger trawlers costing more to run and carrying bigger crews could nevertheless only land an average of less than 2 cwt. after a day's fishing, an undoubted indication that there had been a dramatic reduction in the North Sea haddock population during this period.

Complete extinction, however, seems very unlikely to occur among fish, but the future of the larger species of whales gives cause for grave concern. Indeed, unless international agreement can be reached to limit the number of each species which the whalers of the world are allowed to catch, some of them must become extinct in the comparatively near future. This will be a loss not only to the animal life of the world, but to man himself, who will have lost for ever the valuable contribution which these large whales make to his economy.

Although the main task of this book is to examine the status of animal species which are still living, and which can therefore still be saved if threatened with extinction, some mention must be made of species which have been annihilated already. Since 1800 some fifty mammal species and a much greater number of birds have disappeared for ever.

Perhaps the most remarkable example of extinction by commercial exploitation was that of the North American passenger pigeon. When the white man first went to America and began to push westwards he discovered what must have been the greatest existing concentration of birdlife existing anywhere in the world. The total numbers of these birds must have been astronomical, and even individual flocks might contain countless millions of birds. One exceptionally large flock recorded by the great American ornithologist Audubon took several hours to pass, although flying at speeds of something like sixty miles an hour. He estimated that this flock contained well over one thousand million birds, which is about five times as great as the total number of all the birds in Britain.

To make any significant impression upon these enormous numbers, let alone destroy the entire species, would have seemed quite impossible. Yet within a few decades in the second half of the last century the passenger pigeon joined the ranks of the other unfortunate animals which had become extinct through man's intervention. In the early days of American colonisation the passenger pigeon was a godsend. It was good to eat and it was ever present and easy to kill. The settlers themselves, however, could not possibly have made any significant inroads on the pigeon populations. The real doom of the species dates from the time of the construction of the transcontinental railroad. With the railway came the professional pigeon killer, who realised that consignments of the pigeons sent back to the eastern towns could bring in a great deal of money. Killing pigeons was ridiculously easy. Both barrels of a shotgun fired in quick succession at a flock on the wing could bring down at least one hundred birds, and netting at night could trap three thousand birds or more in a single net. By the 1860's, when the pigeon slaughter reached its peak, a hunter could earn as much as £10 a day, and £10 in the 1860's was really worth something.

By the 1880's it was already clear to a few experts that unless an immediate halt was called to the pigeon slaughter they might all be destroyed. No heed was paid to their warnings, and by 1900 only a few isolated specimens remained alive. The doubtful distinction of having been the last passenger pigeon left alive belongs to Martha, who was hatched in 1885 and died in Cincinnati Zoo in 1914. Today her body is on exhibition in the U.S. National Museum in Washington, as a powerful reminder that however numerous a species may be at any particular time, there can be no guarantee against future extinction unless constant vigilance is maintained.

Hunting for what might be described as pleasure, as distinct from hunting commercially valuable animals, has also played a part in reducing animals' numbers in the past, though today the big game hunter is himself facing extinction, partly because of the prohibitive cost of organising safaris and partly through restrictions which have been increasingly imposed upon his activities in recent decades by governments anxious to preserve their dwindling wildlife. The dangers which these so-called 'sportsmen' brought to the continued existence of the Kodiak bear during the latter part of the nineteenth century are described in the next chapter.

The threat to animal life through hunting has, however, since the last war taken a new turn with the development of spear fishing by skin divers. The majority of skin divers in shallow coastal waters are content to see at first hand the beautiful animal life of the off-shore waters and the coral reefs. Unfortunately a minority dive with spears with the express intention of killing as many fish as they can, despite the fact that most of these rock and coral reef fish are quite inedible and therefore without any commercial value. But through their efforts they are denuding many coasts of their once abundant vertebrate fauna. In the West Indies and in other similarly favoured regions whole coastlines have been practically cleared of fish. One enthusiast has been reported as boasting that he succeeded in virtually wiping out all the larger rock fish around one of the smaller West Indian islands within a space of ten years.

One of the most recent and sinister threats to wildlife has come from an extension of the activities of the fur trade since the war. By the 1950's the trade outlook was not too good. Young women no longer regarded the ultimate possession of a mink coat as the height of their ambition in fashion. Indeed they were tending to regard the fur coats worn by their mothers and their friends as 'square'. Clearly, then, the fur trade would have to come up with fresh ideas if it was to attract the patronage of the younger generation.

It was out of these difficulties that the new 'fun furs' emerged. Traditionally the fur coat was a winter necessity for people living in cold climates, as it still is today. Only much later did it become a status symbol, with a mink coat as the final goal. But even these socially desirable coats were warm. The new emphasis was to be upon appearance, with warmth as a very secondary consideration. All kinds of furs which had hitherto scarcely warranted the attentions of the furrier were now being shipped in great numbers to the main markets of the world, and greatest attention was paid to one animal, the leopard. By the early 1960's the leopard coat had replaced the mink coat as the most desirable of all.

Until it acquired this suddenly elevated status the leopard had never given cause for concern about its future survival. Both in

Africa and in Asia leopards were numerous, and the numbers shot by the big game hunters and captured for zoos represented only a minute proportion of the total populations. By 1964 it was estimated that the annual export of leopard skins from East Africa alone had reached something like 50,000, the majority being accounted for not by licensed killing but by large-scale poaching and smuggling. Illicit trading in leopard skins had become the most profitable and skilfully organised racket in East Africa.

Quite clearly no animal could survive exploitation on this scale for many years. The position is becoming desperate, and as leopard skins become scarce so the price goes up, and as the price goes up so poaching becomes more worth while because the rewards are greater. Here is a clear case for public opinion to exert an influence on utterly ruthless commercialism. The fur trade understands quite clearly the inevitable consequences of its present policy, but so far has shown no willingness to reduce its demands for leopard skins to a level which would give one of the most beautiful of the wild cats a chance to survive.

Although pressure is greatest on the leopard, other wild cats are also being sacrificed on the fun fur band wagon, including tigers, jaguars, cheetahs, pumas and many of the smaller spotted cats, like the South American ocelot.

Perhaps the attitude of the fur trade can best be summed up by the following extract from an advertisement which appeared in *Harper's Magazine* in 1967. After listing no fewer than eighty-eight different kinds of fur coat which the furrier could supply, he adds a footnote on the Himalayan snow leopard, incidentally one of the most beautiful and one of the least common of all the larger wild cats. 'Unfortunately a Himalayan snow leopard perfect enough to become a Max Bogen fur hasn't been sighted in over two years. But you can be sure that when the right one comes along, it'll end up at Max Bogen.'

The wholesale destruction of the leopard in East Africa has brought home to the farmers the importance of maintaining the balance of nature as no theoretical arguments could possibly have done. In every part of the world the natural balance between predators and their prey is an extremely important factor in maintaining the status quo. The consequences of any significant interference with the balance of nature can be much more serious than is generally realised. Leopards prey mainly upon baboons and bush pigs, both of which can cause great devastation of crops if their numbers are allowed to increase drastically. And this is just what has happened. The virtual elimination of the leopards has enabled these two species to increase to plague proportions, necessitating special measures to protect crops from excessive devastation.

It is not only the skins of fur-bearing animals which have been subject to greatly increased demand in recent years to the detriment of animal life. Reptile skins are also very much in fashion for shoes, handbags, wallets and other luxury leather goods. Thanks to this turn of fashion the American alligator is seriously threatened. Until recently there was no cause for anxiety, but in the past few years unprecedented poaching on behalf of the leather trade has been causing grave concern. In 1966 it was estimated that about 50,000 alligators were illegally caught in Florida alone.

Another important, but this time necessary threat to animal populations arises from the increase in human populations all over the world, and the attempts to improve their standards of living. Conservationists recognise that as more land is brought under cultivation to meet these needs, so less remains available for wildlife, which in consequence must accept a reduction in numbers. What they are anxious to ensure is that sufficient of each species shall remain to guarantee its continued existence. To demand that no such diminution should be tolerated would be to fly in the face of the facts of twentieth century realities.

Excessively large herds of domestic animals can also play a significant part in the reduction of wild animal populations by overgrazing the land, thus destroying the vegetation on which both they and the wild animals depend. As we shall see in Chapter 4, the native wildlife of a particular area is capable of utilising the native plant life much more efficiently than introduced domestic cattle, and is thus much less likely to convert fertile areas into deserts. So often domestic cattle have little more than prestige value, providing little in the way either of meat or milk.

Domestic cattle, too, are great carriers of disease, which they can transmit to wild animals. The steady rehabilitation of the Great Indian rhinoceros was seriously threatened by rinderpest contracted from local domestic cattle carrying the disease, as described in Chapter 2.

Poaching has already been mentioned as a contributary factor in the reduction of wildlife. Animals are favoured by poachers for a variety of reasons, but whatever the reason the poacher must be assured of an adequate financial reward. There are two main reasons for poaching, luxury and food. Luxury can include the shooting of animals for commercially valuable skins, or in the case of elephants for their ivory tusks, or for parts of the body which have commercial value because of some alleged medicinal property, like the horn of a rhinoceros. The other main reason for poaching is to obtain meat, either for the family of the poacher or for sale. Taken together the activities of poachers are playing an important part in the annihilation of animal species.

Interference with the balance of nature by the introduction of alien species or by excessive destruction of one of the native species can have a profound effect upon the native animal life, and can well endanger hitherto thriving species. The classic example of extinction is the dodo, an extremely large flightless member of the pigeon family, inhabiting the island of Mauritius, where it was first discovered by visiting Dutch sailors in 1598. From that year its numbers were steadily reduced by other sailors who called in on their voyages across the Indian Ocean. These depredations it might well have survived, but its fate was sealed when the first Dutch colonists arrived in 1644, bringing with them pigs and dogs. Between them these introduced animals succeeded in annihilating the dodo in less than fifty years. By 1693 the dodo had achieved the doubtful distinction of being the first animal species whose extermination could be fully documented.

Flightless birds like the dodo can only survive in areas where there are no native predators. The many flightless birds of New

Zealand have enjoyed this immunity until recent times, but like the dodo their downfall has been animals from other lands introduced by settlers. The drastic effects of introduced animals upon the kiwis of New Zealand are described in Chapter 7.

One of the most disastrous introductions of recent times has been that of the North American musk-rat (*Ondatra zibethica*) into the U.S.S.R. Fur-bearing animals are of course extremely important in this cold sub-continent. In the attempt to increase the available numbers of fur-bearing animals a number of musk-rats were introduced from Canada to the island of Karagin. The rate at which they acclimatised themselves and proceeded to multiply was so encouraging that in 1932 groups were introduced in various parts of the Russian mainland, where again they multiplied so rapidly that by 1935 it was already possible to start trapping the animals for their fur, known as musquash to the trade.

Before these introductions Russian zoologists had warned that introduced musk-rats would compete with certain native fur-bearing animals, particularly the desman (*Desmana moschats*), a valuable animal which lives in many Russian rivers, but the warnings were ignored. As a result, not only is the desman becoming scarce in rivers and lakes where the musk-rats have become established, but the effects of its arrival upon the fauna in general has been equally disastrous. In 1951, eighty-one musk-rats were released in Lake Christee. By 1962 a survey showed that more than half the species of animals which had previously inhabited the lake had been completely destroyed, and those which still remained were much reduced in numbers. The net result of the introduction of the musk-rat to Russia seems to have been that a valuable fur-bearing animal capable of living alongside the existing fauna is being replaced by a less valuable species which is causing wholesale destruction among them.

The selective destruction of one member of an existing fauna can produce equally unfortunate results. The perfect demonstration of the unexpected consequences of such destruction occurred in the early years of this century in the U.S.A. In a mistaken effort to increase the deer herds on the Kaibab plateau President

Theodore Roosevelt, himself a very keen naturalist, authorised the destruction of the natural enemies of the deer, the puma and the wolf. The result was not as expected. Deprived of their natural enemies, which had served to keep their numbers in check, the deer multiplied so rapidly that there was soon insufficient grazing to support them. As a result what had been fertile grassland capable of supporting large herds of deer was soon reduced to unproductive desert virtually unable to support any wildlife. As their available food supplies diminished so the deer died of starvation in their thousands, and in a very short time the total deer population fell far below what it had been when they were subjected to the full effects of their natural enemies.

The value of natural predators to the animals on which they prey has much more recently been confirmed in the U.S.A. On Isle Royale, an island national park in Lake Superior extending to 210 square miles, moose have always been abundant. Their numbers fluctuated considerably, however. They would reach a peak of two or three thousand and then decline rapidly, because they had so outstripped the available grazing that large numbers of them died of starvation. Over a period of years the numbers would gradually creep up again until the population was once more decimated by starvation. After these mass deaths even those which survived were in poor condition, and they remained in a weak state until the grazing had had a chance to recover.

During this period of population fluctuation the moose had no natural enemies. During the winter of 1949, however, following one of the periodic starvation cycles, a pack of timber wolves crossed the fifteen miles of ice from the Canadian shore. Today both the moose and the grazing are always in good condition. The wolves prevent the moose population growing sufficiently to outstrip its food supply. Their culling, however, is selective, the vast majority of those killed being either old or sick, thus leaving the strongest and healthiest to provide the next generation. As a result Isle Royale now has one of the most flourishing moose populations in the whole of North America.

The capture and export of excessive numbers of certain species of animals is another important factor leading to dangerous reductions in numbers. Live animals are exported in large numbers for three main reasons: to maintain supplies to zoos, to supply the large demands for certain species used in medical research, and to supply the pet trade.

No animals live for ever even under the most favourable zoo conditions, and unless an animal is one of those which breeds readily in captivity, then when it dies it has to be replaced from the wild. Eventually this steady replacement demand can have a serious effect upon the wild stocks. At the present time the future of the monkey-eating eagle, *Pithecophaga jefferyi*, a magnificent eagle living on the islands of Mindanoa and Luzon in the Philippines, is in jeopardy because the rate of capture for the zoos of the world exceeds the annual reproduction rate. Because of the serious position the members of the International Union of Directors of Zoological Gardens have agreed not to buy these rare birds until the wild population has had a chance to re-establish itself. Unfortunately a stuffed monkey-eating eagle on the sideboard is regarded as a status symbol by the inhabitants of the Philippines, and this adds to the perils facing the species at the present time.

Various species of monkeys have become extremely important in medical research and in the preparation of vaccines, particularly polio vaccine. It has been calculated that the annual turnover in monkeys by the medical profession is something like 25,000. The demands fall mainly upon a few species, and it is questionable for how long these species can meet such demands without becoming in danger of extinction. Unless some substitute methods of producing these vital vaccines can be developed within a very short time, several species must face imminent danger within a decade.

Another recently realised danger to wildlife in many parts of the world has come from the development of more effective pesticides. As agriculture becomes more efficient so the need to control crop pests becomes more urgent, and the agricultural chemists have devoted a great deal of time and energy to synthesising compounds to meet this need. In the early 1960's it became clear that a certain group of chlorinated hydrocarbons, notably aldrin, dieldrin and heptachlor, while undoubtedly extremely effective in controlling pests, were proving increasingly harmful to many wild animals. Their great disadvantage, it was discovered, was that whereas most other pesticides were fairly rapidly destroyed when they fell on the ground, these three persisted in the soil for years, and tended to accumulate, since each year's spraying reinforced the persisting residues from previous years.

The first effect of these organo-chlorine insecticides is a gradual accumulation in the bodies of worms, insects and some small animals. These in turn are eaten by birds, which thus acquire their own accumulations, the effects of which may be eventually to kill them or to make their eggs infertile. Once the dangers of the chlorinated hydrocarbons had been established beyond doubt the Minister of Agriculture stepped in, and on 24 March 1964 he banned the use of aldrin, dieldrin and heptachlor except for certain very special purposes.

In India the threat to wildlife through the use of these compounds has taken rather a different turn. Here the farmers have been using them directly as poisons to kill tigers, leopards and other large animals, either by adding a few ounces to the animals' kills, so that they are poisoned when they return to them, or by scattering poisoned bait along their known tracks. In Kerala elephants have also been killed by distributing infected bananas.

The last cause of rarity is a completely natural one, unconnected with the activities of man. As indicated in the first paragraph of this chapter, animal species do become extinct in the normal course of events, often because they are being replaced by more efficient successors. At any point in time therefore there will be certain species of animals which are reaching the end of their allotted span. The giant panda, *Ailuropoda melanoleuca*, is probably an example of an animal facing natural extinction. It was an extremely rare animal when it was first discovered by Père David in the forests of South-West China in 1868.

In the final chapter we shall meet some animals which have only been discovered during the last decade or so. Animals which have eluded discovery for so long are almost certain to be rare, and if they are to be saved from extinction when they do become known, they require the utmost vigilance and protection.

We have now dealt fairly comprehensively with the first part of our original composite question, why do animals become rare and perhaps extinct, and must turn to the third part of the question in order to examine the ways and means of saving threatened species. The answer to this part of the question is of course as varied as that to the first part, and the two answers are closely related, since the reason for any particular species facing extinction usually points to the method of preserving it.

The most effective method of preserving any animal threatened with extinction is for the country in which it lives to grant it absolute protection, which means that no one may kill specimens or capture them and send them abroad. There are three ways in which this can be achieved. A general prohibition order forbidding killing or capture can be effective if the animal is generally distributed in the country. If it is confined to a restricted area, then this area can be declared a sanctuary for the animal. Where there is a need to protect not only the one species but a number of other native species as well, this can best be achieved by setting up a national park, where all killing is forbidden. Many animals are migratory, living in different areas in the winter and summer. Therefore to be effective reserves and national parks must include both habitats as well as the migration routes between them, otherwise the protection given is only partial.

The fact that man's activities were endangering wildlife, and that increasing numbers of animals were likely to face extinction, was only really recognised towards the end of the last century. As soon as the facts became known enlightened people began to found societies to take an active part in wildlife conservation. The first of these national societies was the Society for the Preservation of the Wild Fauna of the Empire, which was founded at a meeting held at the Natural History Museum in London on 11 December 1903. In 1950 its title was changed to the Fauna Preservation Society. Throughout its long career it has been one

of the leading bodies concerned with fauna preservation all over
the world. By the 1930's similar preservation societies had been
developed in almost every country in the world.

After the Second World War it was clear to everyone concerned
with the future of wildlife that human pressure upon the animal
kingdom was still increasing, and that even greater efforts would
be needed if large numbers of species were not to disappear for
ever in a few decades. As a result of this world-wide concern the
International Union for the Conservation of Nature was founded
in 1948, with the aim of coordinating the activities of all the
separate societies throughout the world, and to cooperate with
governments in whose territories any threatened animals were
living.

The Survival Service Commission of the Union was set up
subsequently to supply up-to-date information about every
animal species in danger or likely in the near future to be in
danger of extinction. During the past two decades scientists of
the Commission have carried out invaluable investigation work
in many parts of the world. In 1966 the Commission published
their *Red Book*, which in two separate volumes listed 277 species
of mammals and 321 bird species at that time considered to be to
some degree in danger. Both volumes are loose-leaf books, with
each species occupying one page. As soon as any change takes
place in the status of any species, subscribers are sent a new page
to replace the one originally issued. With these books anyone can
follow the progress of all modern conservation efforts. Also
associated with the International Union is the World Wildlife
Fund, whose aim is to collect money from all parts of the world
to help finance the often costly conservation projects.

However alert the various conservation bodies may be, it seems
almost inevitable that certain threatened species will in the end
suffer extinction in the wild. The numbers of some animal
species may already have fallen below the minimum necessary to
guarantee their survival even with complete protection, or the
authorities of the countries in which they live may give no heed
to the warnings and pleas of the conservationists. Even if a species
is finally doomed to extinction as a wild species, preservation is

still not impossible provided measures to build up breeding stocks in captivity are taken in time.

Zoos throughout the world today realise that their most important role is saving threatened animals from extinction, and that they can only do this by learning how to breed these animals in sufficient numbers in captivity. This task is not as easy as it sounds and involves constant experimental work designed to discover the optimum conditions under which any particular species will not only thrive but will also breed in captivity. The results of this work have shown that conditions which will enable a particular animal to survive and live to a ripe old age may not allow it to breed satisfactorily. The conditions needed for successful breeding are undoubtedly more critical than those needed for successful survival.

Since the end of the last war much of the work of zoos all over the world has been geared to the task of discovering the optimum breeding conditions for as many wild animal species as possible. Zoos no longer act as isolated units. In 1948 the International Union of Directors of Zoological Gardens was founded. Its aim is the complete exchange of all information concerned with the keeping and breeding of wild animals in captivity. At its annual meeting all advances made during the previous year are discussed. As a result every zoo in the world is made aware of any important discoveries made by any individual zoo in its attempts to establish breeding stocks of any species of wild animal.

In June 1964 an international symposium organised jointly by the International Union for the Conservation of Nature, the International Union of Directors of Zoological Gardens, the International Council for Bird Preservation and the Fauna Preservation Society was held at London Zoo. The main discussions at this extremely important conference centred around the necessity of breeding threatened animals in captivity so that they might eventually be returned to the wild if the original wild populations became extinct.

Having considered the first and third parts of our original composite question, we must now say something about the second part—why should we attempt to preserve wildlife? The arguments fall into two groups, economic and aesthetic or moral. The need to conserve animals which are economically valuable will be obvious to any business man, who will appreciate the possible consequences of extinction to his own or others' pockets. Even so he may well be prepared to risk destroying a species provided that in doing so he can make a quick profit for himself. Some of the larger species of whales are facing extinction today because the international whaling fraternity are not prepared to settle for a somewhat lower profit in order to ensure the continued existence of animals upon which their prosperity depends.

To convince people and governments that the destruction of species will upset the natural balance of the communities of which they form a part is not such an easy task. In most cases it is impossible to forecast with any degree of accuracy what the effect of the elimination of one member of a community may be. One can only point to many examples showing what actually has happened in the past following the disappearance or serious reduction of a species. The only certainty is that such removal will result in other changes in the community as a whole, and these changes tend to be detrimental rather than otherwise.

The aesthetic argument is one which should hardly need to be put. To most people surely the reasons for preserving the animal and plant life of the earth are similar to those for preserving great buildings and great paintings. To elaborate here would in any case be a waste of space and time, for it is unlikely that a convinced destructionist would be tempted to read a book about fauna preservation.

Chapter 2

Some Important Early Preservation Successes

RECOGNITION of the very possibility that the activities of man could bring about the extinction of an animal species only dawned during the latter decades of the last century and the first years of this, and even then it was only an enlightened minority who were able to grasp the solemn truth. So dedicated were some of these early preservationists to the cause that their successes provide some of the classic models upon which later conservationists have drawn both for inspiration and guidance. In this chapter I have included six of these classic examples, without which no account of fauna preservation could possibly claim to be complete. In subsequent chapters we shall be concerned in the main with efforts made during the last few decades, and aim to give some idea of the present position of and the future prospects for the world's animal life.

Perhaps the most spectacular of man's unfortunate efforts at extermination was his almost complete annihilation of the American bison, or buffalo as it was more usually called. In the days of its abundance, which lasted practically into the middle of the nineteenth century, the bison (*Bison bison*) roamed over most of the North American plains in numbers which are almost impossible to imagine. It has been estimated that at this time there were not less than sixty million of them. In the spring they migrated northwards to enjoy the fresh young grass which grew up rapidly after the winter snows had melted, and in the autumn they returned southwards before the snows reappeared. A single herd might well consist of up to four million animals.

To the native Indians the bison had always been the universal providers, yielding a high-grade meat similar in taste and texture to beef, but with an added gamey flavour, skins with which they made their homes as well as their clothing, shoes and bed covering, and horn from which they fashioned spoons and other utensils. Even the bisons' sinews were used to make their bow strings. Bison hunting was done on horseback using the bow and arrow. Although large numbers must have been taken each year to satisfy their needs, the Indian tribes made not the slightest inroads upon the total bison population, nor did their other natural enemies, the wolves and grizzly bears. Indeed their position must have seemed impregnable.

The downfall of the bison really began when the white settlers began to move westwards during the latter part of the eighteenth century. Contact between the white men and the Indians resulted in trade between them, the white man wanting bison skins to keep him and his family warm in the winter, and the Indian wanting rifles, realising that with them he could kill many more bison.

Even with these new firearms, however, it is extremely unlikely that the Indians could ever have made any great inroads on the vast bison herds. What really did trigger off their decimation was the construction of the Union Pacific railway right across the continent from east to west. Huge numbers of workers were involved in this construction work, and they had to be fed. The cheapest way to feed them was to kill the bison which teemed everywhere.

Before long, as the line steadily penetrated further west, commercially-minded hunters realised the financial possibilities of shooting the bison and transporting them back to the growing eastern towns, whose populations constituted a great untapped market. Although there was some demand for the bison meat, it was the hides and the tongues, the latter being regarded as a delicacy, which could be sold in unlimited quantities. So the practice grew up of taking the hides and tongues of the bison and leaving the remainder of the carcase to rot on the plains. By the middle sixties the great bison slaughter was in full swing, with at least two million animals being killed every year. By 1883 the whole vast area of North America had been virtually cleared of bison, with the exception of one small herd, estimated to be about

10,000 strong, still roaming about North Dakota. In September of that year a party of hunters set off with the avowed intent of wiping it out, and this they did. With this last act it seemed that the American bison had ceased to exist.

That such an enormous population of such a large animal could have been decimated in such a short time seems almost beyond belief. Equally incredible is the fact that although what was happening must have been widely known, and its implications obvious to at least some people, so far as we know no protests were raised. The whole population of North America was apparently quite content to see one of its largest animals disappear for ever. Not until after the Dakota slaughter were the first voices of conscience raised.

Fortunately the change of heart was not too late, for although the hunters were rejoicing in the belief that they had not left a single bison alive, in a few isolated and out-of-the-way parts of the continent there were small pockets of undetected survivors. Some of these were carefully looked after by farmers, in a state of semi-domestication, and they managed to build up small breeding herds. A census taken in 1889 estimated the remnant population throughout Canada and the U.S.A. at 541.

From now on an all-out effort was made by the newly-formed American Bison Society, with the blessing and cooperation of the Federal Government and the New York Zoological Society, to re-establish the American bison as a viable species safe from any future danger of extinction. Fortunately the bison proved to be an animal which will flourish both in captivity and under national park conditions. Since that time the numbers have increased steadily, the 10,000 mark being passed during the 1950's, the vast majority of today's bison living either in national parks or zoos. Modern conditions of both urbanisation and agriculture are hardly compatible with millions of half-ton animals careering northwards or southwards on twice-yearly migration stampedes. As the middle west was opened up from the 1860's the bison herds would have had to be reduced to small fractions of their original sizes, but this could have been done under proper control which would not have put the species in jeopardy.

At about the same time as travellers from the middle west were describing the vast bison herds, early explorers and hunters in South Africa were writing about almost equally large herds of a curious-looking antelope called the white-tailed gnu (*Connochaetes gnou*), a relative of the well-known and still abundant brindled gnu or wildebeest (*Connochaetes taurinus*). The white-tailed gnu, sometimes called the black wildebeest, does not look much like a typical antelope. It is more like a small pony with horns which curve down the sides of the head and then turn up at the tip.

The behaviour of the herds was by all accounts as eccentric as the appearance of the individual animals. Gordon Cumming, one of the great hunter-naturalists who were such a feature of the mid-nineteenth century African scene, has left a wonderfully graphic description of their antics.

'Wheeling about in endless circles,' he wrote, 'and performing the most extraordinary varieties of intricate evolutions, the shaggy herds of these eccentric and fierce-looking animals caper and gambol round the hunter on every side. While he is riding hard to obtain a shot at a herd in front of him, other herds are charging down wind on his right and left, and, having described a number of circular movements, they take up positions upon the very ground across which he rode only a few minutes before.'

'Singly, and in small troops of four or five individuals, the old bull wildebeests may be seen stationed at intervals throughout the plains, standing motionless during a whole forenoon, coolly watching with a philosophic eye the movements of the other game, uttering loud snorting noises, and also a short sharp cry which is peculiar to them. When the hunter approaches these old bulls, they begin whisking their long tails in a most eccentric manner; then springing into the air, start prancing and capering, and pursue each other in circles at their utmost speed. Suddenly they all pull up together, when the bulls will often begin fighting in a most violent manner, dropping on their knees at every shock; then, quickly wheeling about, they kick up their heels, whirl their tails with a fantastic flourish, and scour the plain enveloped in a cloud of dust.'

Although many other African antelopes can still be seen in large herds, these gnu herds are gone for ever, though fortunately the species still survives. Many animal species have been brought to the verge of extinction because of their commercial value. The white-tailed gnu has the rather curious distinction of having been almost annihilated because of its inferiority. When the Dutch farmers settled on the plains they discovered that meat from the gnus was inferior to that from other antelopes. Accordingly they fed themselves and their families on the choicer species, taking care not to shoot too many of any one kind and endangering its future. The white-tailed gnu, however, they considered was quite good enough for feeding their numerous native labourers. Accordingly immense numbers were killed every year. There were so many of them initially that the possibility that indiscriminate slaughter could ever seriously threaten the species never occurred to the farmers, and it was only towards the end of the century that they woke up to the fact that what had once been the most abundant animal species on the plains had now become one of the rarest. Fortunately an enlightened minority decided they must take steps to halt the decline before it was too late, and to initiate measures to preserve the remnants of the species.

As a first step they rounded up as many survivors as they could find, with the intention of building up a number of semi-captive herds on some of the larger farms. By 1899 about five hundred had been gathered together and divided up into about fifteen herds of various sizes, each herd being under the care of a farmer determined to maintain and increase it. The number of survivors was similar to that of the American bison in 1889, but whereas the revival of the bison went smoothly, the white-tailed gnu has proved a much more difficult animal to save. It seems that it is such a gregarious species that only in really large herds will it flourish. In smaller herds, even perhaps of a hundred or more, insufficient herd 'spirit' seems to develop, and consequently breeding only occurs intermittently. This has been confirmed at zoos and zoological parks, where small herds of almost any other normally gregarious animals breed well and increase steadily. They find that about the best they can hope for from a similar gnu herd is that it will produce offspring just about fast enough to replace those which die, mostly of old age. However, there has been a very slow increase in numbers since 1899, and today the total world population is certainly more than one thousand.

The European bison (*Bison bonasus*), the only relative of the American bison, was also reduced to a remnant requiring special measures to protect it from final extermination, but the reasons for its decline were quite different. As mentioned in the first chapter, an animal may become seriously reduced in numbers because its natural habitat becomes reduced for some reason. The European bison is essentially an animal of the forests, feeding upon such grasses as it can find in the clearings. In very much earlier times, perhaps up to the end of the sixth century, almost the whole of northern and central Europe was covered with primeval forest throughout which vast herds of bison are believed to have roamed. From this time onward, as agriculture developed, so the forests were reduced in extent, but the process was slow, and it was not until the end of the eighteenth century that only a single area of the once immense forest remained. This was the Puszca Bialowieska covering a few thousand square miles in Poland. As the forest dwindled over the centuries, so the bison herds disappeared one by one, until it has been estimated that by this time the sole survivors in Bialowieska forest numbered somewhere between three hundred and five hundred. Soon after this the forest became a private hunting ground for the Tsars of Russia, which meant that for the next century or so the bison enjoyed the strictest possible protection. But whereas with protection they should have increased, their numbers very slowly declined, until at the outbreak of the first world war there were probably not more than about two hundred of them. We now know that the most probable cause of their comparative failure was competition. In addition to the bison, vast herds of red, fallow and roe deer were maintained in the forest for hunting, and more recent experience has shown that deer in sufficient numbers will compete successfully for the most nutritious food. If bison have to make do with second grade food they do not flourish.

The war itself was disastrous for the remaining bison. During 1919 the retreating German armies passed right through the forest where they were engaged in heavy fighting with the Lithuanians. Some time later the Polish Army fought a series of battles here with the Russian revolutionary army. The combined result was that when peace was finally restored in the area not a single bison remained alive. Fortunately a few small groups which had been assembled in their private parks before the war by landowners interested in animals had survived the war, as had a certain number of specimens in a few zoos.

These remnants were now the sole survivors of the species, which made it at that time one of the rarest of all the larger wild animals. Special efforts would be needed to avert final extinction. At a meeting in Paris in 1923 an International Society for the Protection of the European Bison was formed. In view of the fact that some of the owners of European bison had at some time or another crossed their stocks with American bison in the hope of getting more vigorous animals, the first task of the Society was to examine each herd in order to determine which animals were still pure-bred European.

This work resulted in the publication of the Pedigree Book of the European bison in 1932. The authors were able to list only thirty pure-bred bison, contained in five small groups in Britain (Woburn), Germany, Holland, Poland and Sweden. By careful management the total had reached nearly a hundred by the outbreak of the Second World War. There were no serious losses to reduce the numbers significantly during the war, though adequate feeding was not as easy as in normal times. A new edition of the Pedigree Book in 1947 was able to list ninety-eight living specimens.

The aim of all conservation measures for species which have become extinct in their natural habitat is eventually to reintroduce them to the territory which they once occupied. The return of the bison to the Bialowieska Forest has taken place in two stages. At first a small nucleus herd was introduced into an area of five hundred acres which had been fenced off from the remainder of the forest. Then, in 1956, a small nucleus herd was released into the open forest. Both groups have been doing well and breeding freely. The free herd now numbers over thirty, the majority of which have been born free, and the world total approaches four hundred, which means that a species which after the First World War faced the threat of imminent extinction seems to be safe for the foreseeable future.

In those early days of fauna preservation dating from the end of the last century and continuing into this, with which we are mainly concerned in this chapter, the Dukes of Bedford at their great animal park at Woburn in Bedfordshire played an important part in saving three of the species considered here. As we have seen, theirs was one of the small nucleus herds of pure-bred European bison from which the present much larger stocks have been built up.

In 1881 the Polish explorer Count Przewalski, returning from one of his expeditions, travelled across Mongolia, a country about which very little was known in the west. Here he discovered a new kind of horse, but was only able to bring back one skin with him. Nevertheless European zoologists were very interested in it and in the description Przewalski gave of the horse and its habits. At this time it was believed that no genuine wild horses still existed anywhere in the world, all the wild ancestors of the domesticated horses and ponies having become extinct in pre-historic times. It seemed possible to the experts, however, that this horse might be a genuine wild survivor from the remote past. But before any positive pronouncement could be made they would have to examine a complete specimen, and preferably a living one. Mongolia, however, was so remote, that a full-scale expedition would be the only hope of obtaining any of the horses.

It was at this point that the 11th Duke of Bedford performed one of his greatest services to the cause of zoology. He commissioned the great German animal collector, Carl Hagenbeck, to obtain six specimens for him. With these he intended to build up a small herd at Woburn, where they could be studied by zoologists at leisure. The epic expedition, led by Wilhelm Grieger, one of Hagenbeck's most experienced men, occupied well over a year, but after a return journey on foot lasting eleven months he was at last able to hand over twenty-eight Przewalski horses to Hagenbeck in Hamburg in 1901. The Duke of Bedford got his nucleus herd, and the remainder were distributed to various European zoos. It was not long before the experts were able to announce that *Equus przewalskii*, as they called it, was indeed a genuine wild horse, and therefore an animal of more than usual interest and importance.

The arrival of these twenty-eight Przewalski horses turned out to be an even more important event than could possibly have been realised at the time. Not only were they the only specimens ever to arrive in Europe, but within twenty years the horses had apparently completely vanished in the wild state leaving the off-spring of the twenty-eight as the sole survivors of the species, which thus at this time disputed with the European bison the doubtful distinction of being the world's rarest mammal. Certainly in 1881 and in 1900 the wild horses were plentiful on the Mongolian plains. What had happened to wipe them out by 1920 no one had the slightest idea.

The small captive herds on which the future survival of the species now depended did not do as well as had been hoped. By 1950 the total captive population was only about thirty, consisting of two small herds each about a dozen strong, and a few isolated individuals. Even the Woburn herd was on its last legs, and in fact the last survivor of the offspring of the six which had arrived there fifty-four years before died in 1955. Since then, however, there has been some improvement in the status of the species. A few more small herds have been founded with nucleus stocks from the two main herds.

At the same time it has been discovered recently that the species is not in fact completely extinct in the wild state. Even prior to the last war rumours began to reach the west that some horses might still survive in Mongolia, and after the war this was confirmed. The number still living, however, would seem to be small. In 1966 Dr Kaszab, Director of the Zoological Department of the Hungarian Natural History Museum in Budapest, led an expedition to western Mongolia, during the course of which a small group consisting of seven mares and one stallion were sighted in a remote and uninhabited region close to the Chinese border. It seems clear, however, that the number of survivors must be small. Dr Kaszab suggested in his report that it was essential to establish the exact whereabouts of the remnants of the species, and then to apply the strictest preservation methods if they were to be saved from final extinction.

If the Dukes of Bedford have played important roles in the conservation of the European bison and the Przewalski horse, the present survival of the Père David deer (*Elaphurus davidianus*) is entirely due to their efforts. When the French missionary Jean Pierre Armand David discovered the deer which now bears his name in 1865 it existed only in the walled Imperial Hunting Park to the south of Peking. It had already become extinct as a wild species in China, and had existed nowhere else in the world. During the next few years he was able to send a few specimens back to Europe, and these found their way to various zoos. After 1870 no more arrived from China, but the small European stocks were kept going with a certain amount of breeding.

Suddenly, however, two disasters wiped out the Chinese herds in Peking, and the few European specimens assumed great importance as the sole survivors of the species. The first disaster occurred in 1894, when severe floods breached the walls surrounding the Imperial Hunting Park in several places. Many of the deer escaped into the surrounding countryside where, despite strict laws protecting them, they were killed and eaten by the starving peasants. Although much depleted, the herd within the walls was able to continue until 1900, when the second disaster took place. This time it was the foreign troops sent to Peking to quell the Boxer Rising who killed virtually all the surviving Père David deer. Small numbers did escape from the park, but these did not survive for long.

The species was saved by the prompt action of the 11th Duke of Bedford. He realised that the many small groups present in zoos and private parks in various parts of Europe would not be able to build up to form viable herds. The only hope for the future was to collect together all these small groups and isolated individuals to form a single herd. With the willing cooperation of all owners of the deer he was able to assemble what was then the total world population, and give them the freedom of his 3,000 acre park. Even so there were only eighteen specimens. These desperate efforts were successful, and by the outbreak of the 1914 war it seemed that the species was already well on the way to becoming re-established, for the Woburn herd now numbered eighty-eight, and the annual rate of breeding was steadily increasing.

During the war it was impossible to give the deer any supplementary rations, and the resulting acute shortage of food meant that many of them died. Enough survived, however, for the build-up to be continued after the war, and by the outbreak of the Second World War in 1939 the herd had increased to about two hundred head. During this war they fared better, and within a few years after it had ended the number of Père David deer at Woburn approached four hundred.

By this time, however, important developments affecting the future of the species had already been initiated. In 1943 the 12th Duke, who had succeeded his father a few years earlier, and who was equally dedicated to the cause of animal life and its preservation, decided that the time had come to build up other subsidiary herds from the Woburn stock. He was worried lest some calamity should befall the Woburn herd, in which case the species could become extinct at one single blow. Such an event might result either from a bombing attack on Woburn Park, or through an outbreak of disease, such as foot-and-mouth disease.

As a result of discussions with the Zoological Society of London, of which he was a council member, it was agreed that attempts would be made to build up a subsidiary herd at Whipsnade. From this herd, once it had been established, it was proposed that small groups of deer should be distributed to various parts of the world so that as many small offshoot herds as possible might be built up. It was recognised that the more herds there were, the less was the likelihood of the species being exterminated through some calamity.

To set up the first subsidiary herd at Whipsnade was not as easy as it might have seemed, however. Père David deer are large animals, and adults could only be captured with great difficulty and with the possibility of damaging them. It was accordingly agreed that a small number of day-old calves should be taken from the Woburn herd and sent to Whipsnade, where they would be hand-reared until capable of caring for themselves. Accordingly, in 1944 two calves were sent from Woburn to Whipsnade as a pilot scheme.

The experiment was completely successful, and the two male calves were successfully reared. They were followed by the transfer of several calves during each of the next few years, until a flourishing but small herd capable of perpetuating itself had been established. Within another year or two small groups were being sent out from Whipsnade to found herds at other zoos in various parts of the world. The most important of these distributions took place in 1957, when a keeper of the Zoological Society left London to deliver four calves to Peking. In this way Père David's deer returned to its native country after an absence of nearly sixty years. This, like the other herds in various parts of the world, is doing well, and it seems quite safe to claim that the species has been finally saved from any possibility of future extinction.

We come now to our sixth and last classic example of animals which were on the verge of extinction at about the turn of the century and which are now reasonably safe because of pioneer measures initiated at that time. Altogether there are five living species of rhinoceros in the world, two in Africa and three in Asia. At the beginning of this century the two African species were still plentiful, but the three Asiatic species were all in great danger. Chief among these was the great Indian one-horned rhinoceros, *Rhinoceros unicornis*. Up to at least the eighteenth century it is known to have been common and widespread throughout northern India and neighbouring countries. But by the end of the nineteenth century it could be found only in parts of Assam, Bengal and Nepal, and even here it was extremely rare. A survey undertaken in 1904 estimated that probably not more than a dozen or so specimens remained in the Kaziranga district of Assam, while elsewhere in the province it was already extinct. A similar number were believed to survive in Bengal, while in Nepal, although no figures were quoted, it was also known to have become extremely rare.

The virtual extermination of the rhino was due in the main to the rather curious commercial value placed on its horn. In all eastern countries, but particularly in China, rhino horn had the reputation of being the perfect aphrodisiac, and accordingly fetched an extremely high price. All parts of the animal could in fact be sold, but it is doubtful whether it would have come so perilously near to extinction if it had not been for the value placed upon the horn. The meat had a ready market because even the Brahmans were permitted to eat it. The hide, too, was used to make all kinds of articles, and even the urine was credited with antiseptic properties. To add to these incentives to kill the rhinos for commercial reasons came the nineteenth century vogue for 'sport', which usually meant shooting as many animals as possible just for the fun of it.

Besides all these reasons contributing to the decline of the rhinos there was the effect of the spread of agriculture. As we have already mentioned in the first chapter it is inevitable that wild animals should have their habitat limited as the agricultural needs of native populations increase. The natural habitat of the Indian rhino is open savannah covered with elephant grass growing to a height of some six feet. As the population of India grew over the past few centuries much of this natural cover was cleared to make way for cultivation. As their territory was reduced, the rhinos retreated to the hill country, where for some time they were safe from human development. Eventually, however, even this type of country came under man's encroachment, for it was in the hill country that he cultivated his most productive tea plantations.

When, however, the true position of the Indian rhino was at last realised, at the beginning of the century, the authorities acted with commendable speed. In 1908 the Kaziranga area was designated a rhino reserve by the Indian government, and in 1926 the whole area was declared a sanctuary, in which all animal life was accorded complete protection. These prompt measures were very successful. By 1930 the Kaziranga rhino population was estimated to be not less than one hundred and fifty. Even now, however, the rhino was not safe. By this time the value of rhino horn had become so great that it was worth considerable risk to obtain it, and consequently the authorities found themselves up against determined poachers. Severe measures taken by the government in 1933 succeeded in reducing poaching to an insignificant level, so that by the end of the Second World War the number in the Sanctuary was estimated at about four hundred. It seemed therefore that the great Indian rhinoceros had at last been saved from the possibility of extinction.

Now, however, it was disease which threatened the rhinos. This they contracted from domestic cattle in the area surrounding the sanctuary. As a precaution a team of staff and students from the Veterinary College of Gauhat visited the whole area surrounding the Kaziranga Sanctuary inoculating all the domestic cattle against rinderpest, to which rhinos are also susceptible. Altogether some 50,000 head of cattle were inoculated. These measures seem to have been successful, for today the rhinos in Kaziranga have fully recovered from the effects of disease, and their numbers have risen to at least their previous peak of four hundred.

What had been happening to the rhinos of Nepal during all this time was not known until the late Mr E. P. Gee, who had been responsible for the measures for conserving the rhinos of Kaziranga, made a survey of the rhino position in Nepal in 1959. He estimated that the population numbered at least three hundred. Thus scarcely more than half a century after the great Indian rhinoceros had been faced with imminent extinction, it can reasonably be considered to have been saved.

Chapter 3

Operation Oryx

ONE OF the most spectacular and important recent attempts to save a species from an apparent threat of imminent extinction has been the all-out effort to save the Arabian oryx (*Oryx leucoryx*). Ever since the last war the status of the species had been causing anxiety in conservation circles. In earlier times the oryx, essentially an animal of the desert, had been widespread and numerous throughout the Arabian peninsula and as far north as Palestine and Jordan wherever there was suitable terrain. By the 1950's, however, it was only reliably known to survive along the southern fringe of the Rub-al-Khali desert, and perhaps along its eastern fringe as well. By 1959 the number of oryx surviving in this area was estimated to be somewhere between eighty and one hundred.

The extermination of the oryx over most of its previous territory had been due almost entirely to hunting. Because of its great strength and endurance the Arabs always had a great admiration for the oryx, and believed that by killing and eating it they would acquire some of its qualities. Hunting it on camels and using traditional weapons was not very easy, and did not have a great effect on the populations. The introduction of modern firearms and motor vehicles, however, put the oryx herds in jeopardy.

Hunting from cars was first introduced by American and British employees of the oil companies, but was soon adopted by the Arab rulers, who organised enormous hunting parties in which as many as three hundred cars might take part.

The situation suddenly became critical when, in December 1960, a motorised expedition from Qatar on the Persian Gulf crossed the Rub-al-Khali desert with the express intention of hunting the last remaining Arabian oryx. They remained for

several weeks, during which time they are known to have killed
at least forty-eight oryx, probably more than half the total
surviving population. At once the Fauna Preservation Society
and the International Union for the Conservation of Nature
conferred on the possibility of taking measures to conserve the
remainder of the herd. It was decided that it was impracticable
to set up a reserve in Arabia because of the impossibility of
enforcing any protective measures which might be agreed upon.
The only hope seemed to be to capture a small nucleus herd and
transfer them to some suitable habitat where they could be
looked after and given complete protection.

Even while they were discussing their plans a second hunting
raid from Qatar was reported in December 1961, in which at
least sixteen of the much depleted population were killed. How
many were now left was not known, but it could be less than
two dozen. The final plans for the capture of the nucleus herd
—'Operation Oryx'—were agreed at a meeting at the Fauna
Preservation Society in London in August 1961. The operation
itself was timed for April and May 1962, before temperatures
should rise to such an extent that chasing the animals would cause
them dangerous distress. Any animals captured would be sent in
the first place to Isiolo, in the northern province of Kenya, where
the Kenya Game Department would look after them while they
adjusted themselves to captivity, and until they could eventually
be transferred to their permanent destination.

The personnel chosen to take part in the expedition, and the
organisations backing it, made it a truly international effort, and
provided an excellent demonstration of what could be done by
such cooperation to save any animal species threatened with
imminent extinction. The leader chosen for the expedition was
Major Ian Grimwood, Kenya's chief game warden. His assistant,
a man with all the local knowledge, would be Mr M. A. Crouch,
Assistant Advisor, Northern Deserts, Eastern Aden Protectorate.
It was in fact Mr Crouch, knowing at first hand how critical the
position was, who pressed for an immediate rescue operation.
Other personnel came from Kenya, Aden and Britain. Financial
assistance was given to the Fauna Preservation Society by the

World Wildlife Fund, the London *Daily Mail* and many interested individuals. The East African Wildlife Society lent their Piper Cruiser spotter aircraft with Mr C. K. Gracie to pilot it, while the Hadhrami Beduin Legion under its commandant, Lieut. Col. J. W. Gray, undertook all the administration in the field, providing very efficient units of men and vehicles, and maintaining a radio link with the outside world. The R.A.F. undertook to transport all the members of the expedition and its equipment to Aden, including the Piper aircraft, which was brought in in the hold of a Transport Command Beverley.

The expedition with all its stores was assembled during April 1962 at Mukalla, a coastal town about three hundred miles east of Aden. All the stores, including fuel and tents, were taken over by the Hadhrami Beduin Legion, who had undertaken to transport them to the advance base, which was to be their fort at Sanau, in the north-west of the Aden Protectorate. The expedition finally left Mukalla at 0800 hours on 23 April. It took them seven days to negotiate the difficult terrain which finally brought them to Sanau, a distance of about five hundred and fifty miles from Mukalla. Major Grimwood acknowledges that without the help of Quaid Gray and his Hadhrami Beduin Legion the operation would have been virtually impossible.

If any oryx still remained alive in the Protectorate they would be found in this north-western extremity. The large store attached to the fort was converted into pens in which any oryx captured could be kept until it was possible to get them away. In view of the speed with which oryx move it was decided that the best method would be to chase and noose them from a moving vehicle. The party had previously undertaken an expedition to capture the beisa oryx in Kenya, which had given them an opportunity to perfect their technique. The beisa oryx, a powerful animal weighing some 400 lbs., had given them some trouble after it had been noosed, for it had struggled hard, and its long straight horns had been a source of considerable danger.

Tomatum Bin Harbi, an Arab who knew the territory well, had by now joined the expedition to act as guide. It was he who knew where any surviving oryx might be found. The prospects were not very bright: although the Hadhrami Beduin Legion garrisons at both Sanau and Habarut had been asked to keep a special watch for oryx for the past few months, no signs of their presence had been reported. The actual search lasted from 30 April until 21 May, during which time only four oryx were captured, and evidence of the existence of only seven others was gained. It thus looked as though the two hunting parties had indeed come very close to exterminating the oryx of the Aden Protectorate. The search had been very thorough both on the ground and from the air, and had embraced some 6,000 square miles. One of the captured animals soon died, and a post mortem examination showed that it had a recently fired ·303 bullet embedded in one haunch, which probably caused its death.

Thus when on 27 May a R.A.F. Beverley took off from Sanau for Aden it carried only three captured oryx, two males and one female. At the airfield a Britannia was waiting to carry them to Nairobi, where they were disembarked at 15.30 hours. Here they were to rest until the next day, when they were due to continue their journey to Isiola, where the Kenya Game Department had built special pens to receive them. On landing, however, Major Grimwood was greeted with the disturbing news that there was a serious outbreak of foot-and-mouth disease at Isiola, and that infected cattle had been very near to the pens. It would thus be extremely risky to take the oryx there at this time.

Mr John Seago, the animal collector, who had his headquarters at Nairobi, offered accommodation for the oryx until it was considered safe for them to be transferred to Isiola. Isiola had been chosen because of its dry climate, somewhat similar to that of the Arabian desert, whereas Nairobi's climate was damp. Nevertheless the three oryx settled down well after heating had been provided in their quarters. Six weeks later, when it was deemed safe to transfer them to Isiola, they were in excellent condition, and seemed to have adjusted themselves to captivity and the new foods with which they were provided.

Isiola, however, was only an intermediate stage in their journey. It had been decided that the best hope for building a flourishing breeding herd would be for the animals to be taken somewhere with a climate resembling as closely as possible that of the Arabian desert, and arrangements had been made for the Phoenix Zoo in Arizona to make themselves responsible for the herd. Accordingly on 20 May 1963 the three oryx were flown from Isiola to New York via London, where they were joined by London Zoo's female, presented to the Fauna Preservation Society by the Zoological Society. The four spent a month at the United States Animal Quarantine Station at Clifton, New Jersey, before finally being transferred to Phoenix Zoo on 24 June.

Before the three left Isiola one of the males had been observed to mate with the female, and on 26 October a male calf was born. By this time the herd had been further increased by the gift of a third female—the only one in his private zoo—by the Ruler of Kuwait. Thus by the end of 1963 the Arizona herd consisted of two adult males and three females, and one male calf.

By this time, however, H.M. King Saud of Saudi Arabia had announced his intention of presenting two males and two females to the World Wildlife Fund to be added to the Arizona herd. When Major Grimwood went to Saudi Arabia in March 1964 to collect them he found a small but flourishing herd of thirteen oryx in a zoo which had been opened six years earlier at Riyadh. At the time of the 'Operation Oryx' expedition the existence of this herd was unknown outside Saudi Arabia. The discovery of its existence was cheering since it constituted an important second string to the Arizona herd.

Soon after their arrival in Arizona the herd was increased to eleven by the birth of a second male calf, this time to the London Zoo female. Although the subsequent birth rate has been quite satisfactory, and gives every hope that a really large herd can be built up, there has been a preponderance of males among the calves, and males do not increase the breeding potential of a herd once there are sufficient of them to mate with the females. The third and fourth calves, both males, were born in December 1964 and May 1965. The fifth and sixth, again males, were both born in August 1966. Then at last came the first female calf in September 1966, bringing the herd total to sixteen. A second female was born in January 1967, but the herd strength remained at sixteen because one of the two males born the previous August, a weak calf at birth, had died a few days before.

By May 1968 the total number in the herd had increased to eighteen, of which seven, including two calves born in March and May 1968, were females. In 1967 the Los Angeles Zoo managed to buy a pair of oryx, and these have so far produced two female calves, thus giving a good start to the second herd in North America.

'Operation Oryx' and the world-wide publicity and backing which it received, focused attention on the Arabian oryx. As a result further information about its status in the wild came to light. During 1962 and 1963 groups of Bedouins travelling through Oman reported sighting small groups of up to twelve individuals. Consideration of this and other evidence suggests that some two hundred oryx may in fact still exist in Oman. These are reasonably safe from the local populations since the Sultan has forbidden hunting of them. Unfortunately such protection does not guarantee absolute safety, since they would still be at the mercy of a motorised hunting expedition originating in some neighbouring state. However keen the Oman authorities might be to conserve their remaining oryx herds, the fact remains that it is a practical impossibility to patrol thousands of square miles of uninhabited desert. So until a new climate of opinion about protection of the oryx becomes generally accepted through-out southern Arabia one can only hope that these recently dis-covered herds may escape the attentions of the wealthy hunters.

Although not generally known at the time, the success of 'Operation Oryx' and the attention it focused on the plight of the Arabian oryx, was responsible for the foundation of another captive herd. In 1962 Sheikh Qassim bin Hamad al Than, the Qatar Minister of Education, became so concerned about the possible fate of the oryx that he decided to assemble a small herd on his estate some fifty miles from Doha, the Qatar capital. By January 1968 the herd numbered twenty-four and breeding records are good. On his own confession, the Sheikh had himself been a keen hunter, but was converted when he realised what he and his fellow hunters had done to the once numerous herds of oryx in Arabia. It is quite possible in fact that he may have taken part in the 1960 and 1961 raids from Qatar already described. In 1966 he emphasised his conversion by becoming a life member of the Fauna Preservation Society with a generous donation of £100. Today the responsibility for building captive stocks of oryx is shared by the Sheikh. Unfortunately most of the remaining animals in the Saudi Arabian herd were sold to a Dutch animal dealer in 1965.

The subsequent discovery that wild herds of oryx still existed in Oman, and a second flourishing captive herd in Qatar, in no way detracts from the importance of 'Operation Oryx'. Certainly the foundation of the Qatar herd, and most probably the protection now given to the species in Oman, are entirely due to the efforts of the Fauna Preservation Society and the World Wildlife Fund to make known the desperate plight of the species. Without their efforts it is unlikely that either of these measures would have been taken, in which case the species might well have become extinct by now.

Chapter 4

Problems of Conservation and Preservation
in Africa

THE KEY to any understanding of the conservation problem as it affects Africa is that this vast continent contains by far the richest collection of fauna to be found anywhere in the world. Mammals, birds and reptiles exist in abundance and bewildering variety. Yet what remains today is but a meagre remnant of the teeming mass of animal life discovered by the European explorers who first penetrated the interior of the 'dark continent'.

From time immemorial the native populations of Africa had lived in harmony with their animal neighbours, using them as a source of meat and to exercise their hunting powers. But, as with natives elsewhere in the world, they constituted no threat to any species. With the opening up of the continent through the arrival of the white colonisers, however, came the inevitable threat to the wildlife. Great areas of forest were cut down to make way for agriculture, and immense numbers of palatable animals were killed to provide meat for a steadily growing population.

Thus today whole areas have become almost denuded of their larger game animals. Fortunately, however, Africa is so vast, and its original stocks of animals so enormous, that relatively few species have disappeared altogether. Most species can still be found inhabiting at least part of their original habitat. The steady reduction in animal life which has taken place over the past one hundred years or so has not been brought about with any sinister intent. It has been mainly the inevitable consequence of the fact that arable farming cannot be successfully prosecuted in areas containing large herds of antelopes and other herbivorous animals, and that dairy farming and cattle ranching cannot be very successful in a district teeming with lions. Gradually, therefore, the wildlife of Africa has found itself pushed back into areas not yet made available for development.

Poaching, both by natives and by whites, has in recent times also made a significant contribution to the reduction in numbers of certain species which can provide products of high commercial value. Thus leopards are endangered because of the value of their skins, as also are crocodiles and pythons, while elephants and rhinos have the misfortune to possess tusks and horns for which there is a ready and financially very rewarding market.

The first full realisation of the threat to African wildlife posed by modern developments must be credited to President Kruger of South Africa, who as early as 1884, long before he became president, brought to public attention the fact that the animal life of the Transvaal was diminishing at an alarming rate, and that unless something was done to stem the tide no animal life might be left. He proposed to the Transvaal parliament that a certain area should be set aside where animals could be protected from all future persecution. His colleagues, quite unmoved by his pleas, rejected his proposals out of hand.

But Kruger was not to be put off by one reverse, and in 1888 he again drew the attention of the Transvaal parliament to the increasingly urgent necessity of setting aside some parts of the country where all hunting would be prohibited. This time his resolution was accepted, but nothing was done about it.

He had, however, influenced some members of parliament who examined his proposals, and in due course, on 6 September 1895, they submitted a motion which was to have far-reaching consequences: 'The undersigned, seeing that nearly all big game in the Republic have been exterminated, and that those animals still remaining are becoming less day by day, so that there is a danger of them becoming altogether extinct in the near future, request to be permitted to depart from the order paper to discuss the desirability of authorising the government to proclaim as a Government Game Reserve, where killing of game shall altogether be prohibited, certain portions of the district of Lydenburg, being Government land, where most of the big game species are still to be found, to wit, the territory situated between the Crocodile and the Sabi Rivers with boundaries as follows.'

The boundaries they suggested were those finally adopted when the Sabi Game Reserve was proclaimed by President Kruger himself on 26 March 1898. Thus was founded the first true game reserve. For more than a quarter of a century there was a great struggle between the supporters of the Reserve and the vested interests which had all along been against its establishment. Final triumph was not achieved until 31 May 1926, when the National Parks Act was passed, under the terms of which the Sabi Game Reserve became the Kruger National Park. By this time the value of a national park as a tourist attraction had been recognised, and today the Kruger is one of the great tourist attractions of the world. It has also become a wonderful living museum of the majority of the animal life of South Africa.

The success of the Kruger National Park set the ideal pattern for wildlife conservation as it was applicable to Africa, where the need was not for the complete protection of selected species, as it was in most other parts of the world, but for the conservation of a complete sample of the fauna of an area. The success which followed its establishment led to the creation of reserves and national parks all over Africa, and even today hardly a year passes without the founding of others.

After the last war, with independence being granted to one African country after another, it was feared that all the work which had been put into the national parks would be wasted, because the new rulers would identify fauna conservation with their former white rulers, and would accordingly want to reverse their decisions. In the event these fears proved to be unfounded. The new rulers of Africa realised the importance of well-run national parks as a tourist attraction. Hence the continued establishment of such parks.

It was realised by the world's leading conservationists and conservation bodies that for the new governments of Africa to recognise the importance of conservation was only a first step. In implementing their resolves to protect the animal life of their territories they would face great problems, financial and otherwise. If they were to translate theoretical support for the cause of wildlife preservation into practical conservation they would need help and encouragement.

With this end in view the general assembly of the International Union for the Conservation of Nature, held in June 1960 in Warsaw, launched their African Special Project. This was to be a three-stage programme. The first phase entailed a visit by Mr G. G. Watterson, Secretary-General of the International Union, to the majority of the countries of west, central and east Africa in order to discuss with their governments the principles and problems involved in wildlife conservation. The second phase was a conference held at Arusha, Tanganyika in September 1961 to discuss conservation in modern Africa and to formulate plans for future action. The third phase was the establishment of an expert unit which would be available to help and advise any African government on all problems arising from their attempts to put conservation measures into effect.

Typical of the reception which Mr Watterson received was the following introduction by Chief Fundikira to a conference on 'Land Management Problems in Areas Containing Game' held at Manyara, Tanganyika, in February 1961. 'My colleagues and I in the Government see game as one of Tanganyika's great national assets. At all costs it must not be allowed to waste away. But it must be worked, as an asset, for all it is worth. It must not just look like an asset; it must prove itself and be seen to be an asset, and one worth husbanding carefully if it is not to be wasted. The enemies of game are the men who grudge it living room, grazing and water, who fear its depredations and covet its trophies, regardless of cost. We must provide for all of them. But above all we must work out ways of convincing the man who imagines himself to be immediately threatened by game that it is to his ultimate advantage to keep game in being. One of the ways we must study is that of associating the local authorities of these people more closely in the management of the game in the area. Another possible fruitful approach—if fruitful is the right word when we have butcher's meat in mind—is the cropping of game to supply proteins for the people's diet. But I won't go into greater detail. I very much hope that out of this conference there will come advice and ideas which will help me to make clear to the people of Tanganyika, to whom I am responsible, that what I am personally convinced of is true. I mean that without its game, Tanganyika would be a poorer place.'

The Arusha Conference was attended by one hundred and thirty delegates representing between them nearly all the countries of Africa and all the international conservation organisations, as well as the United Nations Food and Agricultural Organisation (F.A.O.). The general feeling of the meeting was summed up in the Arusha Manifesto presented by Mr J. K. Nyerere, Prime Minister of Tanganyika.

'The survival of our wildlife is a matter of grave concern to all of us in Africa. These wild creatures amid the wild places they inhabit are not only important as sources of wonder and inspiration, but are an integral part of our natural resources and of our future livelihood and well-being. In accepting the trusteeship of our wildlife we solemnly declare that we will do everything in our power to make sure that our children's grandchildren will be able to enjoy this rich and precious inheritance. The conservation of wildlife and wild places calls for specialist knowledge, trained manpower, and money and we look to other nations to cooperate in this important task, the success or failure of which not only affects the continent of Africa but the rest of the world as well.'

Many other countries made reassuring declarations of their intentions, and in a final resolution the conference confirmed 'the earnest desire of modern African states to continue and actively expand the efforts already made in the field of wildlife management. These countries recognise their responsibilities and the rightful place of wildlife management in land use planning.'

Stage three of the African Special Project was inaugurated at a meeting of the I.U.C.N. in Morges, Switzerland, on 27 January 1962, at which Mr P. R. Hill and Mr T. Riney were appointed as the working team to operate under the joint sponsorship of the I.U.C.N. and the F.A.O.

As a footnote to this short account of the African Special Project the following statement by the Kenya Government is worth quoting. It was made at the General Assembly of the I.U.C.N. held in Nairobi, Kenya, in September 1963 and signed by Mr Kenyatta, the Prime Minister, and two of his ministers.

'The national resources of this country—its wildlife which offers such an attraction to visitors from all over the world, the beautiful places in which these animals live, the mighty forests which guard the water catchment areas so vital to the survival of man and beast—are a priceless heritage for the future. The Government of Kenya, fully realising the value of its natural resources, pledges itself to conserve them for posterity with all the means at its disposal. We are confident of the cooperation of the other governments of East Africa in this important task but, at present, we are unable, unaided, to provide the specialist staff and money which are necessary. We therefore invite other nations, and lovers of nature throughout the world, to assist us in honouring this solemn pledge.'

It should be abundantly clear from what has already been said that modern Africa is in the main conservation minded. There are problems, however, some of them grave, and in the remainder of this chapter we shall examine some of the most important of these.

One of the major problems facing conservationists in Africa is the devastation caused by large herds of domestic cattle. It is now recognised that these primitive cattle are extremely inefficient in converting plant food into meat. They are also indiscriminate grazers. In large numbers they tend to destroy all vegetation and convert what was originally good pasture into semi-desert. In contrast the wild fauna are selective feeders, and even in large numbers they still allow the plant life to flourish. The wild game, too, are able to produce many times the amount of meat from the same area.

In many African countries today an urgent educational programme is being pursued to convince the native tribes that they would be far better off if they reduced their herds of cattle drastically and relied for their meat supplies upon the wild game which would then be allowed to flourish.

Botswana, formerly known as Bechuanaland before it achieved its independence in September 1966, is a prime example of the way in which severe devastation can be caused by over-concentration on cattle breeding. This is a country which still has the largest concentration of plains game in the whole of Africa. Cattle ranching, however, is the country's major industry, notwithstanding the fact that European cattle are not adapted to live on these typical African plains. As a result the cattle are spoiling the ground, and if they are allowed to continue to exist in their present high concentration, they will render large areas unfit both for themselves and for the native game animals.

Drastic reduction of the cattle herds would enable the native game to flourish, and properly exploited they could eventually provide much greater revenue than could ever be obtained from cattle ranching. The tourist industry could also be developed with the establishment of game reserves or national parks.

Zambia has already realised the value of game cropping. In the early 1950's it seemed doubtful whether the animal life of the Luangwa South Game Reserve could ever recover from the effects of over-hunting and poaching which had almost wiped out all the larger species. Effective protection, however, has enabled the game to recover their numbers so successfully that there is now danger of overgrazing. By 1955 the Zambian Government decided that recovery had been so successful that a meat cropping programme could be put into effect. Accordingly it was decided that two hippos, two elephants, and twelve buffalo would be killed each day, using a humane killer which causes instant death without disturbing the herds. The carcases are taken as quickly as possible to a newly-built abattoir where the meat is prepared and deep frozen. It is then taken in refrigerated trucks to the highly populated towns of the copper belt, where it is sold at prices considerably cheaper than those charged for the most inferior beef. Schemes are now in hand to establish herds of various antelopes in areas where the vegetation is too poor for domestic cattle to be settled, including areas where the tsetse fly is abundant. These schemes should result in a great increase in cheap meat supplies, thus making an extremely valuable contribution to the economy of a country in which protein foods have always been in short supply.

Ghana is also planning for future game cropping. Although not originally in the forefront of African countries where wildlife conservation was concerned, the Ghanaian authorities are now making determined efforts to establish effective game reserves. Everything possible is being done to develop the Mole Game Reserve. Roads are being constructed and camps erected. Several villages inhabited by native hunters within the boundaries of the Reserve have been removed. Already, in an area in which game stocks had become very seriously depleted by indiscriminate hunting, antelopes, buffaloes, elephants, lions and many other species are recovering rapidly under protection. It is hoped that within five years the Reserve will become a national park with a considerable tourist attraction, and within ten years it is confidently expected that it will yield a substantial crop of meat. It has been calculated that with proper management the wildlife of Ghana could yield an annual meat harvest worth something like £40 million, which would be of enormous benefit both to the economy of the country and to the health of its people.

One of the greatest problems facing those responsible for managing national parks is the activities of the poacher. Usually poachers live in areas immediately surrounding national parks and reserves. Under cover of darkness there is little chance that they will be detected when they cross the boundary to take their toll of the protected animals, because there are normally only a few game wardens to patrol very large areas.

Dr E. B. Worthington, Scientific Director of the International Biological Programme, is particularly interested in the whole problem of game cropping. He suggests that each park and reserve should be surrounded by a buffer zone in which game cropping is managed in such a way as to provide the maximum sustained yield of wild animals. Some of these animals would be produced within the buffer zone itself, and the remainder would derive from the park or reserve, representing the overflow of animals which would result when any species developed beyond the numbers which the park could support. At present such surplus populations merely leave the park to provide easy prey for the poachers. In these proposed buffer zones cropping would be carried out only by legalised hunters employed by the authorities, and the meat which they produced would directly benefit the local population.

Buffer zone animal cropping has already been established both in Kenya and in Uganda. Elephants have increased so successfully in the Tsavo National Park in Kenya that there is a continuous exodus of surplus animals into the surrounding country. These are now being systematically cropped. A similar hippo cropping and marketing scheme outside the boundaries of the Queen Elizabeth National Park in Uganda has also recently been put into operation.

Some of the larger farmers in South Africa are already engaged in controlled exploitation of the natural game living on their farms. One sheep farmer, for example, who has a herd of some 7,000 springbok on his farm, is culling an average of 2,000 animals a year, thus providing himself with a substantial additional income without in any way threatening the springbok population.

Although game cropping on a large scale is mainly confined to Africa so far as land animals are concerned, the Russians have also shown how an animal faced with extinction can not only be saved but subsequently used to provide a steady supply of meat. Originally the saiga antelope (*Saiga tatarica*), was common and widespread in all steppe country from eastern Europe through Russia and Siberia as far east as Alaska. For an antelope it is quite a small animal, distinguished by an extremely large, almost grotesquely swollen nose.

Several factors were responsible for a gradual decline of the saiga. Nomadic tribes always hunted it for its meat, and with increased human settlement the demand for saiga meat also increased. Gradual climatic changes also reduced the suitable areas in which it could flourish. But these factors alone could not have reduced the saiga to the point of danger. Unfortunately, like the horn of the rhinoceros, the horn of the saiga was prized by the Chinese and other eastern people as an aphrodisiac. To supply the demand the Russians exported hundreds of thousands of pairs of saiga horns to China annually throughout the first half of the nineteenth century at a considerable profit. As a consequence by the beginning of this century the saiga had become a species in imminent danger of extinction. Its total population now numbered probably not more than a thousand individuals, and these existed in many isolated pockets.

In 1919 a law was passed totally prohibiting saiga hunting. For the next ten years or so the saiga population just about managed to hold its own. Then, as though restraint had suddenly been released, the population began to increase very rapidly. Today the saiga is the most numerous ungulate in the Soviet Union, its total numbers being variously estimated at between $2\frac{1}{2}$ and 3 million. The annual harvest is some 150,000 head, yielding about 6,000 tons of high grade meat similar in flavour to lamb, as well as valuable hides which can be put to a variety of uses.

Successful conservation of a single species or of a complete fauna brings problems of its own. Relieved of the man-pressure with which it has had to live for perhaps centuries, a species may increase in numbers to such an extent that its population density becomes too great for the available food supplies. At the present time the two animals which are causing considerable anxiety on account of the startling increase in numbers since they were given protection in certain national parks are the elephant and the hippopotamus.

In December 1959 Mr R. M. Bere, Director and Chief Warden of the Queen Elizabeth National Park in Uganda, estimated the hippo population of the Park at not less than 14,000, and since they all come out of the water at night to graze the surrounding countryside, they were consuming vast quantities of grass, more than the area could supply. As a result of this overgrazing the land was becoming so damaged that not only would it soon no longer be able to provide enough food for the hippos, but antelopes, buffalos, elephants and other grazers would also be facing a food shortage.

The only possible answer to this particular problem was a systematic culling of the hippos until their numbers had been reduced to such an extent that those remaining could take all the food they required without either damaging the land or leaving too little for the other species who also relied upon it. An annual removal of some five hundred hippos over a number of years has enabled the riverside land to recover.

A similar build-up of elephants has been the cause of considerable anxiety in several national parks, particularly the Tsavo National Park in Kenya and the Murchison Falls Park in Uganda. Elephant culling is a much more difficult problem than hippo culling. If hippos are shot there appears to be little effect on those which are left. But the elephant is a much more intelligent and sensitive animal than the hippo. The shooting of one individual will affect the whole herd.

Experiments have been carried out in recent years with immobilising drugs injected by means of a projectile-syringe shot from a crossbow. In a series of experiments carried out in the Kruger National Park in South Africa in 1961 it was found that it was possible to project a lethal dose into an elephant without other elephants standing nearby taking any notice either of the darting or of the subsequent dropping of the victim some minutes later. The Kruger itself has no significant elephant problem at the moment, but it is realised by the authorities that overstocking may become a problem in the not too distant future. An elephant census carried out in 1962 estimated the elephant population in the Park at 1750, descended from a nucleus population of no more than ten in 1905.

The drug used in these trials was succinyl-choline chloride ('Scoline') projected from a distance of about thirty-five yards. The dose required depends upon the weight of the animal to be immobilized. If an animal is shot but only wounded it becomes a danger both to staff and tourists, besides creating unrest among the other elephants in the herd. Too small a dose of immobilizing drug, however, has no such ill effects. The elephant will recover completely without ever knowing it has been darted. The meat of animals killed with Scoline is edible, since the drug is destroyed during cooking, and in any case is ineffective when taken by mouth.

The development of immobilising drugs during the past

decade has enabled conservationists to introduce a new and potentially extremely valuable method of saving land animals threatened with extinction. In essence it entails removing rare animals from areas where they are exposed to uncontrolled exploitation and transferring them to national parks and reserves where they will be protected. The capture of the larger mammals by chasing and roping is extremely difficult without injuring them, but using these drugs makes such an operation relatively easy and safe. In the near future translocation of animals may well become the most fruitful method of saving any species in danger of extinction.

The first animal to have been saved from almost certain extinction by translocation was the white or square-lipped rhinoceros, *Ceratotherium simum*. Two races of this species are recognised, the northern race, *Ceratotherium simum cottoni*, formerly inhabiting parts of the Sudan, the Congo and Uganda, and the southern race, *Ceratotherium simum simum*, which when the white man first came to southern Africa were common and widespread between the Zambesi and Cunene rivers in the north to the Orange and Umfolozi rivers in the south.

Like the rhinos of Asia, the threat to the African white and black rhinos stems from the widespread belief that rhino horn is a powerful aphrodisiac. The current price in Africa is about £5 per pound. Despite extensive poaching, however, the white rhino population of Uganda increased steadily from an estimated one hundred and thirty in 1928 to three hundred and fifty in 1955. For the next three years the poachers began to step up their efforts sufficiently to prevent any further increase. And then they really put the pressure on the species. So disastrous were their efforts that by 1962 it was estimated that no more than eighty remained alive.

The imminent danger of extinction was recognised in the nick of time. For political and population reasons it had not been possible to include any of the areas inhabited by the white rhinos in any of the national parks which had been set up in Uganda, so that they were all living in places where there was no effective protection. It was therefore decided that attempts would be made to capture a small number of white rhinos and transfer them to the Murchison Falls National Park. Anglia Television provided £1,000 towards the cost of the operation in return for the rights of filming it. Between December 1960 and March 1961, the dry season in Uganda, ten rhinos were captured and released in the Park. The group consisted of four adult cows, three half-grown males, and one male and two female calves. Unfortunately two of the cows died soon after being released, but the remaining eight specimens survived to form the nucleus of a future Murchison Falls rhino population.

This first group of rhinos was captured the hard way by pursuing them in a truck and passing a noose around their necks as the vehicle drew level with them. By 1964, when it was decided that the original group should be supplemented, capture by drug-darting had become well established. Using a helicopter to direct the movements of a Land Rover containing a drug-darting party armed with a crossbow, five more rhinos, four females and one male, were successfully translocated to Murchison. There is now every hope that even if all the other white rhinos in Uganda are destroyed by poachers, the Murchison Falls population will be able to develop and save the species from extinction.

The southern race of the white rhino has come much nearer to extinction than the northern race. By the early 1920's the total number of survivors was believed to be not more than twenty-five, all confined to the Umfolozi Game Reserve, which had been established in 1897. In all other areas where it had existed formerly the rhino had long since vanished. For the next two decades its future remained precarious. Then came a sudden population explosion during the 1940's and 1950's, when numbers increased to several hundred. This itself caused anxiety, because the rhinos were beginning to tax the limited food resources of the Reserve. Also certain areas of the Reserve had been set aside for human settlement, and this would further limit the available food for the rhinos. The obvious answer to the problem was to translocate many of the rhinos to other reserves in areas where the white rhino had long ceased to exist but where there were plenty of available food supplies.

Experiments on dart drugging of white rhinos began in 1960 and continued until 1963 under direction of Dr Harthoorn. During this period a variety of drugs was tried, the most successful being one called M99, developed early in 1963 by Reckitts in England. The first target for resettlement was the Kruger National Park. Rhino had already become extinct in the area before the park was founded. By October 1964 eighty-six rhinos had already been transferred, and in November of that year the first calf was seen. A few months later two more were sighted. By the end of 1966 no fewer than three hundred and thirty rhinos had been removed from Umfolozi and translocated to other parks and reserves, four in South Africa and two in Rhodesia. Sixty-three more had been captured and sent to reputable zoos in various parts of the world. It is hoped that at least some of these zoos will be able to establish small captive breeding stocks.

The immobilising technique was first used successfully in 1958 to study the territorial behaviour of the Uganda kob antelope (*Adenota kob thomasi*). It had been developed just in time to play an important part in the rescue of animals caught by the rising waters of the Kariba lake. The great Kariba dam was closed on 3 December 1958, and as the water level subsequently rose large numbers of animals became marooned on temporary islands of higher ground. The rescue of many of these was a comparatively straightforward operation, but a number of black rhinos (*Rhinoceros bicornis*) which became trapped posed a difficult problem. Conventional methods of capture were tried without success, but by using immobilising drugs it was a comparatively simple matter to capture them, load them on to rafts and release them on the shores of the lake.

In 1967 the same technique was used to capture forty-one black rhinos living in populated areas of Kenya where it was impossible to give them adequate protection, and release them in various national parks.

In the same year ten hippos were removed from the Kruger National Park, where they were becoming rather too numerous, to other South African parks and reserves. In this operation certain difficulties were encountered. The first problem to be solved was to secure the drugged hippos in order to bring them ashore. The dangers of bilharzia infection meant that the captors could not go into the water after the hippos. They solved this problem by using a giant road grader which they could drive right into the water. From this mobile platform they were able to manoeuvre ropes and nets and so secure the animals.

The drug M99 had proved so successful with the majority of animals that by this time it had become established as the standard drug for immobilising. With hippos, however, it proved to have one grave disadvantage. So successfully does it relax an animal's muscles that it puts out of action the normal mechanism by which a hippo's nostrils are automatically closed as it submerges. In consequence the drugged hippo is in grave danger of drowning unless it can be roped and hauled out of the water very quickly. Two out of five hippos on which M99 was used were drowned before they could be rescued. For this reason another drug, Sernylan, was used. Although not quite so effective as an immobilising drug, it did not inhibit the nostril-closing mechanism.

There is no doubt that the discovery and development of these immobilising drugs has provided the preservationist with an extremely valuable technique. Almost any animal faced with a threat of extinction can now be removed from a danger area to somewhere else where it can be adequately protected. If, too, the sole survivors exist as a single population, this can now be divided into a number of separate populations by removing some of its members to other suitable areas, thus removing the danger of complete annihilation through some catastrophe such as an outbreak of virulent disease.

Chapter 5

The Orang-utan and some other Asian Problems

WHILE it is undoubtedly true that over the past two decades preservation efforts have been greatly increased in every part of the world, it is also true that during this same period a number of species hitherto considered relatively safe are suddenly threatened with extinction unless drastic steps are taken to protect them. One of the most important of these recently threatened animals is the orang-utan. Ironically, at a time when zoos and zoological societies all over the world have become increasingly aware of their role in the preservation of threatened species, the most important reason for the decline of the orang has been the desire of zoos to exhibit this particularly endearing animal.

The orang-utan is one of the four remaining kinds of anthropoid or manlike apes left in the world today. Collectively they represent one of the great peaks of evolution, this one being surmounted by man himself, who might be regarded as the fifth and highest of the anthropoids. Orangs are found only on the islands of Borneo and Sumatra. The various species of gibbons are also confined to south-east Asia, but are more widely distributed than the orang, while the other two anthropoids, the gorilla and the chimpanzee, are natives of central Africa. Compared with the orang the other three are relatively free from threats of extinction at present.

Until the period between the wars few orangs were exhibited in zoos, and little was known about them. As the public became more familiar with their gentle characters and fascinating personalities they increased in popularity. By the end of the second world war they had established themselves as one of the prime favourites among the zoo public, and joined the small band of animals like the elephant and the lion which every zoo aspired to possess. But whereas the wild pool from which these other popular animals were obtained was sufficient to satisfy the demands of the world's zoos without endangering the future of either species, the world population of orangs was limited.

No reliable estimates exist of the orang populations of Borneo and Sumatra in the 1930's, but it was probably only a few thousand in each island. After the last war the native populations of both islands discovered a lucrative demand for young orangs. Adult and half-grown specimens were much too powerful to be subdued, and unfortunately the only known method of capturing young orangs was to shoot the mothers first. This, besides meaning that two orangs were lost to the wild population for every one captured, also seriously reduced the breeding potential of the population, for every adult female killed deprived it of a number of further young orangs. Once captured the young orangs were so badly looked after that at least half of them died before they could be sold to someone who knew enough about looking after them to give them a fair chance of survival.

By the end of the fifties the pressure was really on the orangs. The urgency of the problem was brought to the notice of the world by Tom Harrisson, Curator of the Sarawak Museum, whose vitally important efforts to save the edible turtle from extinction by developing artificial hatcheries are described in another chapter, and his wife Barbara. The efforts which are now being made by the International Union for the Conservation of Nature supported by the World Wildlife Fund are also in their charge. This is a most propitious arrangement, because no one knows more about orangs in the wild than they do.

In a joint survey published in *Oryx* in 1961 Tom and Barbara Harrisson reviewed the position of the orang as it then stood. This extremely important report formed the basis for all subsequent action designed to safeguard the species from final extinction. At this time Barbara Harrisson estimated that the total number of orangs living in the world's zoos was about 240. Since their average expectation of life was not more than three and a half years, which meant, incidentally, that too little was known about the conditions needed for keeping them satisfactorily in captivity, replacement of those which died would require the annual export from Borneo and Sumatra of about eighty young orangs. Allowing for the deaths of the mothers, and the deaths of about half of the young orangs before they arrived in the comparative safety of the zoos to which they were consigned, it seemed reasonable to estimate that the yearly toll of wild orangs would be about 240, or 2,400 over a period of ten years. Since the total world population was only a few thousand, of which only the young specimens were suitable for capture, it was clear that such toll of the wild populations could only be taken for a few more years before the position became desperate.

Due to the depredations of the 1950's the position was worse than mere statistics suggested. Because of the systematic shooting of mothers in order to capture their young the breeding potential of the wild population had become seriously reduced, there being now a great preponderance of males. Other threatening factors were at work. With the rapid increase of population after the war, and the demand for higher standards of living, land which had previously been virgin forest suitable for orang occupation had been cleared to make way for agriculture. Even more important was the greatly increased commercial exploitation in Borneo of its very valuable timber, which involved the devastation of further vast areas of forest. As a result of these two factors the orang population was split into many small isolated groups, in some of which the female ratio was too low for satisfactory social life and breeding.

We come back to the fact, however, that the greatest single threat to the species was the capture of babies for export at great profit. The legal protection which orangs had been given in Borneo after the Second World War had had little effect on their rate of capture. In such a vast and sparsely populated country effective control of wildlife was virtually impossible. It was all too easy to capture a young orang by killing its mother, conceal it and carry it over to Singapore on one of the many sampans which regularly made the crossing.

Accordingly Barbara Harrisson made the following recommendations. Responsibility for export control must not be left to the authorities of Borneo and Sumatra. With the best will in the world they would be quite unable to control the illegal traffic in orangs. The zoos of the world should curb their desire to obtain orangs at any cost. If they refused to buy orangs which had been illegally caught and exported the bottom would soon fall out of a very lucrative market. Zoos should get together to improve their methods of keeping orangs in captivity so that their expectation of life could be raised. At the same time they should endeavour to discover the conditions needed for successful and frequent breeding in captivity, so that they might breed their own replacements, as was now possible with many other species.

Since these proposals were put forward considerable progress has been made, and although no one could be complacent about the present position of the wild orangs, the general outlook for the species now is somewhat better than it was in 1961.

By 1963 much had been done to close the three main channels through which captured orangs travelled from Borneo and Sumatra to Europe and America. Following representations by the International Union the Singapore authorities tightened their regulations in an attempt to prohibit both the import and export of orangs without an official clearance from the government of origin. Loopholes still existed to the extent that very clever characters sometimes managed to smuggle orangs into Singapore along with a batch of monkeys for which they had obtained a legitimate export permit. Even so orang export was made so much more difficult that it became uneconomic and was therefore less frequently attempted.

That the measures had had considerable success can be judged from the fact that by the summer of 1963 the market price for young orangs had fallen to not more than £25, whereas a year or two before each one might have fetched as much as £300. The imposition of the regulations, however, left the Singapore dealers with some eighty young orangs on their hands, for which they had already paid considerable sums, and which were costing them something like half a crown a day each to feed. In order to cut their losses they began killing the orangs. Some, however, the authorities managed to confiscate.

Besides Singapore, the other two channels through which it had been possible to dispose of illegally captured orangs were Hong Kong and Bangkok. Hong Kong imposed similar restrictions to those adopted by Singapore in 1962, and Bangkok in 1963.

At their meeting in September 1962 the Board of Directors of the American Association of Zoological Parks and Aquariums adopted an important resolution which answered Barbara Harrisson's recommendations that zoos should exercise greater restraint in the exhibition of species threatened with extinction. 'Resolved that in the interest of conservation, the Board strongly recommend to the membership of the Association that all endangered species that are fully protected and adequately managed by their countries, receive the additional protection which we can afford them by our refusal to purchase any wild-caught specimens of these species which are removed illegally from their country of origin and subsequently offered for sale on the animal market.'

This resolution was followed by another at the next meeting in March 1963. 'Resolved that the Board of Directors instruct the Conservation Committee to prepare, annually, a list of animals whose wild population, in the Committee's judgement, would be seriously endangered by new zoo collection, importation and/or exhibition; that this list, after annual review and approval by the Board be published as the "AAZPA Animal Black List" and that AAZPA members be encouraged to support a policy of non-exhibition of such endangered forms.'

1963 was certainly the crucial year so far as the future of the orang-utan was concerned. Besides the various decisions which have already been described, the International Union for the Conservation of Nature also initiated two important projects. The position of the orang populations in Borneo and the dangers which threatened them were only too well known to the Harrissons, but much less was known about the position in Sumatra. It was accordingly arranged that Mr Oliver Milton should undertake a thorough investigation of the orang population there. At the same time he would examine and report upon the status of the Sumatran rhinoceros. The results of his findings are examined later in the chapter.

The other project concerned young orangs which had been captured illegally and subsequently confiscated. These could not be returned direct to the wild because they would probably not survive. Mrs Harrisson accordingly undertook in 1961 to establish a kind of orang training school in the Bako National Park in Sarawak where the aim would be to educate these young orangs in the ways of the wild so that they might eventually be released to join the much depleted genuine wild population. By 1963 it seemed clear that the project would be successful. Rehabilitation, however, proved to be a long, slow process. In the wild state young orangs remain with their parents and rely upon them for guidance until they are at least four years old. It seemed that the orangs in training at Bako would need a comparable period of training before they could be finally released to enjoy a completely independent life. The training programme was extremely time-consuming. The 'tutors' spent many hours each day with their charges, taking them on long journeys through the forest so that they might gradually become accustomed to forest life, and learn how to feed and otherwise fend for themselves. It was an enormous undertaking in which there were no short cuts, but it was also a project which might ultimately save the orang from extinction if the decline of the wild populations could not be arrested.

Oliver Milton's report, submitted in 1964, showed that the position of the orang in Sumatra was essentially similar to that in Borneo. Estimation of orang populations is always extremely difficult, but he was able to say that the total was certainly not more than 1500, and might be as low as 800. The main reasons for the decline to these figures were illegal capture for smuggling and the opening up of the country for agriculture and large-scale tree-felling. Here, as in Borneo, the various measures designed to reduce illegal export were obviously having considerable success: the current black market price for a young orang was the equivalent of about £100, whereas a few years previously it had been as high as £350.

The establishment of the Federation of Malaysia in 1963, and the subsequent hostility between Malaysia and Indonesia, brought a welcome if unexpected relief to the orangs. With the virtual closing of the frontier between the two parts of Borneo, and the almost complete stoppage of small craft sailings between Borneo and Singapore, orang smuggling via Singapore has been almost eliminated. At the same time it seems that a small minority of unscrupulous dealers and zoos are prepared to pay almost any price to get hold of young orangs, caring nothing that such conduct is diametrically opposed to majority zoological world opinion. Tom Harrisson has given it as his opinion, obviously not formed without reliable evidence, that there are institutions which would be prepared to pay at least £1,000, and perhaps more, for a healthy specimen. So long as such unscrupulous individuals and organisations exist, one cannot really attach overmuch blame to some native living scarcely above subsistence level who seizes the opportunity to secure the means of feeding himself and his family for some years to come as a result of one not particularly risky transaction.

With the authorities in Singapore and Bangkok doing their best to stop smuggling, attempts have recently been made to switch these activities to Japan. A law was passed in June 1967 prohibiting the unauthorised import of orangs into Japan. Between that date and March 1968 five animals were confiscated by the Japanese customs and sent to Japanese zoos pending a decision as to what should be done with them.

To say that the threats to the future survival of this particularly important species have been removed would be over optimistic, but at the same time the measures taken over the past few years both by the governments most concerned and by the various world conservation bodies do give cause for increased hope. Between them they are determined that the orang shall survive.

The threat to the world's rhinos caused by the mythical belief in the aphrodisiacal properties of rhino horn has already been mentioned. Of the world's five living rhino species, three belong to south and south-east Asia. The story of the near-extinction of the great Indian one-horned rhinoceros, and of the successful efforts to save it, has already been told. The other two species are still in a very precarious position. Although they are now called the Javan rhinoceros (*Rhinoceros sondaicus*) and the Sumatran rhinoceros (*Didermocerus sumatrensis*), neither name is particularly suitable, for the original range of both species covered much of southern and south-eastern Asia. The Javan rhino, alternatively named the lesser one-horned rhinoceros, was at one time found in northern India and southern China as well as in most parts of south-eastern Asia, including Sumatra and Java. It is very similar in appearance to the great Indian rhino, and its hide has similar neat folds, but it is smaller in size. The Sumatran rhino, like the two African species, has two horns, and is also known as the Asiatic two-horned rhinoceros. It is much smaller than all the other rhinos. Its original distribution extended from Bengal and Assam right down through Burma to Sumatra and Borneo.

The latest available estimates of the total world populations of these two species are between one hundred and one hundred and seventy for the Sumatran rhino and between twenty-four and fifty for the Javan rhino. Despite these figures, the Sumatran rhino is considered to be in greater danger of being wiped out than the Javan species. The reason for this is that the total population of the Javan rhino is concentrated in one small reserve where protective measures are much easier to enforce. The first serious attempts to save the Javan rhino date from 1921, when the Netherlands Indies Government set up the Udjung Kulon Reserve, where the Javan rhino and the Javan tiger could be granted absolute protection. The reserve was in its location one of the most easily protected, because it consisted of a peninsula at the western extremity of the island. It had a length of thirteen miles and a maximum width of seven miles, but the neck of land separating it from the mainland was only half a mile wide. In order to give the rhinos every possible chance of survival and consolidation without interference no one was to be allowed to live in the reserve, even the staff being obliged to live nearby on the mainland. The latest survey conducted by Dr Rudolf and Dr Lotte Schenkel in 1968 showed that there were between twenty and twenty-nine rhinos in the reserve. Most important, they saw the footprints of a calf estimated to be between three and five months old, and also those of a year-old specimen. This was particularly welcome news because for some years no trace of young rhinos had been found, and it had been feared that for some unknown reason the rhinos were no longer breeding.

Until recently, despite the fact that on paper at least the rhinos were given complete protection, poaching remained rife because there were too few guards to ensure the safety of the species. In 1967 a substantial grant from the World Wildlife Fund made it possible to increase the number of guards and to provide them with more adequate equipment. Both the WWF and the International Union for the Conservation of Nature are treating the Javan rhino as a first priority species.

For the Sumatran rhino there is no area where sufficient numbers exist to make a viable population even with complete protection. The individuals are widely scattered in groups varying from a dozen or so specimens to family groups of three or four individuals. What is really needed to ensure the future safety of the species is a fully protected reserve in which there is an already existing nucleus population which could be supplemented by the introduction of other specimens captured in other areas. Using the drug-darting techniques developed in recent years in Africa for the capture and translocation of rhinos and other large animals from one area to another the concentration of some of the present widely-scattered groups into one protected region might well be possible in the future.

Malaya is one of the countries where the Sumatran rhino still exists. The latest survey, published in 1966, gives an estimated population of about thirty animals, scattered in small groups in various parts of the country in dense and inhospitable forest areas. Their preference for this type of terrain gives them some protection from poachers, making it extremely difficult for them to be hunted down, and also means that they are little affected by the great expansion in agriculture which has been taking place in Malaya during the past decade.

This agricultural development, however, has been having a

devastating effect on the seladang or Malayan gaur (*Bos gaurus*), one of the few remaining species of wild oxen left in the world. The seladang prefers lowland river valleys, which are the areas most suitable for cultivation. Since the last war their numbers have been greatly reduced as large tracts of their original habitat have been taken over for cultivation. Many herds two or three dozen strong have already been wiped out, and others are due to follow them. Even in areas where agricultural development has not yet arrived they are faced with other threats. Seladang are dependent upon salt licks, and one of the factors accelerating their disappearance in agricultural development areas has been the destruction of these licks. The threat in the undeveloped areas is also connected with the destruction of salt licks in the construction of dams for hydro-electric power, particularly along the Perak River. Fortunately, however, seladang still exist in some numbers in the former King George V National Park as well as in certain other areas, so that there are good reasons to hope that the species may be preserved, even though in much reduced numbers.

The lion, in the popular imagination, is the great cat of Africa, its counterpart in southern Asia being the tiger. There is, however, an Asiatic lion, *Panthera leo persica*, which was at one time common right across southern Asia from Turkey in the west to India in the east. In the pre-Christian era there were also lions in Europe, especially in Greece. By A.D. 100 the lion is believed to have become extinct in all parts of Europe. From medieval times onwards the lions of Asia have also been exterminated in one region after another. In Arabia, Iraq, Palestine and Syria the majority disappeared during the time of the Crusades, but a few survivors still existed in one or two remote areas up to the early years of the present century. In Persia (Iran) at that time the lion was still quite plentiful in certain areas.

Today, however, it seems certain that the Asiatic lion has become extinct over the whole of its former range with the exception of the Gir Forest in India. Not since 1884 have lions been reliably reported from anywhere else in India. The chief cause of the lion's extermination in one region after another was hunting. Lion hunting, like tiger shooting, was a traditional sport for the nobility and, from the eighteenth century onwards, of the higher ranks of the army. During the time of the Indian Mutiny it is recorded that a certain Colonel George Acland Smith killed nearly three hundred lions by way of recreation.

Most of the Gir Forest lies in the small state of Junagarh, and in 1900 the Nawab of Junagarh decided to give the lions complete protection on the grounds that excessive hunting had reduced their total numbers to between two and three dozen animals. The actual number was probably about one hundred, but the Nawab gave a deliberately misleading figure to discourage further hunting by 'every British Viceroy, Commander-in-chief, Governor of Bombay, Indian Prince and others down to persons of less importance.' Important guests of the Nawab were still sometimes allowed to shoot a lion, but the total number of such concessions did not exceed three in any one year. As a result of this protection the lion population increased steadily, until by the middle 1950's it was estimated to have reached about three hundred, which was probably about as many as the depleted animal life of the forest would be able to support. A report published in September 1968, however, revealed that the actual number of lions in the forest was then far below this estimate, and was in fact somewhere between a minimum of 162 and a maximum of 177.

The greatest threat to the Gir lions today is not hunting but the destruction of their forest habitat by over-grazing. All through the forest there are semi-nomadic groups with herds of half-starved zebu cattle and water buffalo. As Hindus they are not allowed to kill any of their stock, which continue to multiply in an area which cannot adequately support them. The result is extensive over-grazing, which in turn reduces the populations of the wild herbivorous animals on which the lions would normally feed. In consequence they have to rely upon these domestic herds for their food. The owners of the herds accept the depredations of the lions philosophically, regarding them as the price they must pay for the privilege of grazing their herds in the forest. Unfortunately the over-grazing is resulting in a gradual conversion of the forest into desert, so that each year the total area of forest is reduced.

The only way in which a balance can be achieved between the grazing herds and the lions is through a research programme which can establish how many domestic cattle may be supported within the forest without jeopardising the future safety of the lions. We must hope that before too much of the forest has been converted into desert by over-grazing an answer to this problem will not only have been found but implemented. Two zoologists sponsored by the World Wildlife Fund have begun a two-year investigation into the ecology of the Gir Forest, and it is hoped that the results of their work will make it possible to formulate a policy which will ensure the survival of the lions and at the same time allow the continued use of the forest by the native populations.

Besides the lion and the great Indian rhinoceros, India also has two species of deer which have been facing considerable threats of extinction during the past decade or two. These are the Kashmir stag and the brow-antlered deer. The Kashmir stag, *Cervus elaphus hanglu*, is one of the world's largest and most magnificent species of deer, similar in appearance and related to the European red deer and the North American wapiti. It inhabits the wooded mountain slopes of Kashmir at heights from 5,000 feet in winter to 13,000 feet in summer.

Until Indian independence in 1947 the Kashmir stag had always been strictly protected in game reserves by the Maharajahs of Kashmir. Only the elite of the state and important visitors were allowed to shoot it. In 1947 its numbers were estimated at about two thousand, which gave no cause for anxiety about its future. Independence, however, was followed in Kashmir by very unsettled political conditions and military occupation. As a result of indiscriminate hunting the stags' numbers became drastically reduced, until by 1952 there were only about 325 survivors. Improved administration and more settled conditions after 1953 seemed likely to halt the decline. The area in which the majority of the deer lived was declared a sanctuary in 1951, but nothing was done to enforce the declaration, so that poaching continued on a considerable scale, and far too many permits were issued to important residents and visitors to shoot the deer.

When the late Mr E. P. Gee, the leading authority on Indian wildlife, visited Kashmir in November 1960 on behalf of the International Union for the Conservation of Nature, he was only able to report a total of about 250 deer. He emphasised that there was an urgent need for complete protection against poachers and the complete cessation of the practice of issuing shooting permits.

On a further visit in 1965 he found that the number of deer had been again reduced to an estimated 175. On this visit he found a flourishing sheep-breeding farm right in the middle of the sanctuary. The one thousand or so sheep were undoubtedly competing with the deer for food, and the disturbance caused by the farm staff and their dogs must also have been an adverse influence upon the deer. Fortunately the Chief Conservator of Forests for Kashmir and the newly-appointed Kashmir Game Warden accepted his recommendations. As a result the sanctuary is now a designated National Park, and it seems likely that the elimination of sheep-breeding and cattle-grazing will follow. If so the species will have been saved in the nick of time. At the same time it would be prudent to establish a few captive herds in various parts of the world just in case these measures are not ultimately successful.

The brow-antlered deer of Manipur, *Cervus eldi eldi*, was already causing anxiety after the First World War, and in 1934 it was given complete protection. Unsettled conditions during and after the Second World War were against its survival, and by 1951 it was declared extinct by the Manipur Forest Department. In the following year, however, a small colony was discovered among the reed marshes at one end of the Logtak Lake, and in 1954 an area of twenty square miles was declared a sanctuary where it could be protected. In this last stronghold the brow-antlered deer is relatively safe, because the marshes are extremely treacherous for human hunters to penetrate. One great danger remained, however. During periods of flood the water covers the marshes, and the deer are forced to leave their safe retreat for higher ground, where they become easy prey to the hunter in an area where they have no legal protection.

A hydroelectric scheme is now being developed in Manipur which will lower the level of water in the lake. At first it was feared that this scheme might have an adverse affect on the deer, but on reflection it is realised that it will be to their advantage, because it will ensure that the water level will be kept constant at all times. In consequence during the rainy season the sanctuary will not be flooded, and the deer will not have to migrate to higher ground where they are not protected.

No account of the rare animals of Asia, however brief, could be considered complete without some reference to the giant panda, *Ailuropoda melanoleuca*, the endearing black-and-white bear-like animal which has been adopted as the emblem of the World Wildlife Fund. It was first made known to western science by the French missionary-naturalist Père David in 1869. It is an extremely elusive creature living in dense bamboo forests in the border regions of China and Tibet. How rare it is is difficult to estimate, but it is certainly not plentiful. Very few have ever been seen in captivity. Today only three zoos have specimens, London and Moscow zoos having one specimen each, while Peking Zoo has a small group. Peking is the only zoo to have bred the giant panda in captivity, which is hardly surprising since it is the only zoo ever to have possessed a pair. In 1967 London Zoo's Chi-chi was taken to Moscow in the hope that she would mate with Moscow's male An-an, but the visit was unsuccessful. At the end of August 1968 An-an came to London on a return visit, but again the two refused to mate.

That elephants should ever become extinct seems somehow quite inconceivable, and in fact is not at present a possibility which need be considered seriously. One race of the Asiatic elephant, the Ceylon elephant, is however facing considerable difficulties. In earlier times there were extensive tracts of jungle in Ceylon providing adequate territory for all the elephants. There was no temptation for them to stray from the jungle into cultivated regions where they might have been shot by the farmers in defence of their crops. In recent times, however, and especially since the last war, there has been a great deal of forest clearance in order to increase the amount of land under cultivation.

When this work was planned no thought was given to the fact that elephants migrated at certain seasons from one area to another, and some of the newly-cleared areas cut right through the traditional elephant migration routes. A little thought would have ensured that migration corridors were left passing across the new areas of cultivation, so that the elephants could have exercised their ingrained urge to pass from one district to another. The result of this was that far too many elephants were shot while trying to pass from one region to another and finding themselves caught in the newly-cultivated areas. This position is now being remedied, and corridors connecting isolated pockets of forest are being re-established along the traditional migration routes.

Chapter 6

Arctic Animals in Danger

THE VAST Arctic wastes of snow and ice might well be thought to be one area where animal life would be able to thrive without being threatened by intensive agriculture, industry or pressure of human population. Nothing could be further from the truth. In the first place a region which is so inhospitable to the human species must present comparable difficulties to its animal life. The Eskimos who live there rely almost completely on this animal life for their daily requirements. So long as they had to rely upon their own traditional methods the balance was maintained, because they were not equipped to make excessive inroads upon these animal populations. Once the rifle came into their possession, however, they had the means of killing far in excess of their real needs, so that they became wasteful of their valuable natural resources.

Other factors which have served to reduce these Arctic species to an extent where anxiety is felt about their future have been the establishment of airfields, defence bases and meteorological stations.

To the personnel stationed on these outposts, hunting the larger animals of the particular region is understandably regarded as both an adventure and a welcome relief from the boredom of manning an otherwise uninteresting post.

As a consequence of these factors, and others which we shall examine in this chapter, the four largest and most important Arctic mammals: the polar bear, the walrus, the musk-ox and the caribou, are all in considerable danger. Each of these, however, has been the subject of exhaustive investigations and positive conservation measures during the past decade or two, and it is hoped that these measures will ensure the eventual safety of each of these important animal species.

The caribou is the wild relative of the domesticated reindeer, and in northern North America is one of the most important sources of food and other materials for the Eskimos and the Chipewyan Indians. The Eskimos live on the Arctic tundra, the snow-covered wastes to the north of the tree line, while the Indians live on the taiga, the coniferous belt immediately to the south, both extremely inhospitable areas judged by our standards. Because of the reliance of these two groups of people upon it the reasons for the conservation of the caribou need no underlining. Here indeed is one of the most clear-cut examples of the practical need for conservation as distinct from preservation. It is essential that the caribou population be so managed as to continue to supply the Indians and Eskimos with their essential requirements.

For hundreds of years a complex natural balance was maintained between the caribou herds, their natural enemies, Indians, Eskimos and the wolf, and their limited food supplies. This last consisted in the summer of a considerable variety of plant life, including grasses, cotton grasses, birch, willows and sedges. In the harsh northern winter none of these had much nutritive value, and during this period the caribou relied almost entirely upon lichens, which provided little more than a subsistence diet, the animals drawing upon the stores of fat laid down during the summer abundance.

In modern times the reduction of the caribou herds to the point where their continued survival gives rise to anxiety has been due to interference in several ways with the original balance. The availability of food supplies is perhaps the most important single factor in the maintenance of the caribou herds. In the summer there is an abundance of food available, sufficient to support a total population many times greater than has ever existed. It is the winter supplies of lichen which impose severe restrictions upon the numbers which can be kept alive until the following spring. If any area is over-populated during the winter the lichen will tend to be so drastically reduced that it cannot recover its former abundance by the following autumn, so that during the winter which follows it can only support a reduced population of caribou.

Whereas most other plant life, even if drastically reduced by over-grazing, can recover its former abundance in a very short time, lichen once reduced takes decades to recover. In the northernmost limits of the caribou's range it has been estimated that serious reduction of the available lichen can only be fully restored in something like one hundred years, during which time of course the area will be able to support only a much reduced caribou population.

Until recent times the depredations of the native populations together with the activities of the wolves controlled the herds sufficiently to prevent their increasing beyond these winter food supplies, while at the same time being insufficient to reduce their overall numbers significantly. Then came several new factors which between them have resulted in the reduction of the total caribou population to a mere fraction of what it had been for generations. Misguided conservationists, realising the importance of the caribou to the native populations, and realising also that its only natural enemy was the wolf, embarked on a programme aimed at the virtual extermination of the wolf. Its first results seemed completely successful, for the caribou herds increased at a steady rate. Soon, however, there were more of them than the winter supplies of lichen could support, and this resulted in an increasing reduction of this essential plant life, followed by a progressive reduction in the size of the herds through starvation, until they fell far below the figures which had been consistently maintained for centuries.

At the same time these much smaller herds came under far greater human pressure than the species had ever had to endure before. Hunting by the newly-arrived military and scientific personnel has already been mentioned. With their modern rifles the Eskimos found it so much easier to kill the caribou that there was no longer such dire necessity to make the most of each carcase. Plenty more could easily be obtained to replace any that were wasted. The many which were wounded, too, were no longer pursued until they were captured, but were replaced by further killings.

In addition to this direct human pressure, the caribou have also suffered as human activity has grown in their territory from a startling increase in forest fires. These destroy the valuable lichens, along with all other vegetation, but whereas this will regenerate in a very short time the lichens, as we have seen, require decades to achieve their former abundance.

By 1955 the caribou of northern Canada were estimated by the Canadian Wildlife Service to number considerably less than 300,000, compared with a population which was believed to have been not much less than two million at the turn of the century. The last decade, however, seems to have seen the turn of the tide. Motor vehicles have been steadily replacing sled dogs, whose feeding previously accounted for a considerable proportion of the total caribou meat consumed, and increasing numbers of former Eskimo and Indian hunters have since found other employment, which makes them no longer dependent upon the caribou for their supplies. Today the caribou population is estimated to have increased to about 300,000, a number which the available winter food supplies, though much reduced compared with former times, can support without difficulty.

Just as some Eskimo populations rely upon the caribou for most of their material requirements, so are others equally dependent upon the walrus. This species, too, has shown an alarming decrease in numbers during this century, mainly due to increased ability on the part of the Eskimo to kill them, making him much more ready to waste them. This, as we have seen, has also been an important factor in the decline of the caribou.

The walrus, like sealions and seals, is an aquatic mammal belonging to the order Pinnipedia. Structurally it is in fact midway between the other two groups. Like the seals it is without external ear flaps, but it shares with the sealions the ability to turn the hind flippers beneath the body, thus making it more mobile on land than the seals, which can only progress slowly out of water by dragging their bodies over the rocks.

Two species are recognised, the Atlantic walrus, *Odobenus rosmarus*, and the Pacific walrus, *Odobenus obesus*. The differences between them are minor, their external features and habits being virtually identical. The walrus is by far the largest of all the Pinnipedia found in the northern hemisphere, and is only exceeded in size by the enormous elephant seals of the Antarctic. Large males may weigh well over one and a half tons, but one ton is the average. Large and average females weigh about half these amounts.

The short hairy coat which covers the body is a light rusty brown colour, and the skin beneath it is whiteish, but becomes pink when the animal lies basking in warm sunshine. The relatively small head has a curious appearance, with its tiny piggy eyes, a moustache of tough bristles, and a pair of gleaming white canine teeth, which may exceed a yard in length and weigh as much as twelve pounds each. The female tusks are slimmer than those of the male.

Despite their formidable appearance these tusks are not primarily used as weapons. Their real purpose is to dig out the bivalve molluscs on which these large animals feed. The bristles and tongue between them are able to extract the meat from between the shells, which are then discarded. It is said that the Eskimos take out the molluscs from the stomachs of any walruses they slaughter and eat them after washing them in sea water, from which it seems that the walrus swallows the molluscs without chewing them.

The walrus is quite able to take care of itself. Polar bears sometimes try to get a walrus pup, but if the parents are around they seldom succeed. In fact there are recorded cases of a pair of adult walruses driving a polar bear into the water and killing it with their tusks. Apart from man their only effective enemy is the whale.

For centuries past many Eskimo populations have relied upon the walrus to supply almost all their material needs, just as other populations of Eskimos have relied upon the caribou. The walrus supplies meat for the Eskimos and their dogs, blubber for their lamps and stoves, and skins to cover the floors of their igloos and their canoes. Supplying all of these needs provided no serious threat to the walrus populations. Then came the rifle, which enabled the Eskimos to kill walruses far in excess of their material needs, and

Whooping Crane

Above: Indian Rhinoceros. *Below:* Russian Desman

Hawaiian Goose

Mauritian Dodo

Orang-utan

Above: Arctic Caribou. *Below:* Polar Bear

"Tasmanian Tiger" or Thylacine

Pacific Walrus: adult males

Galapagos Tortoise

with it came the realisation that the walrus tusk also had commercial value. From then on walruses were killed not only for their flesh, blubber and hide, but to provide ivory for trade. Some of the tusks were sold as raw ivory, while others were carved to fetch a much higher price, raw ivory being worth up to two dollars a pound, while carved tusks could fetch as much as one hundred dollars a pound.

Whereas in earlier times every walrus carcase was used completely, the realisation of the value of ivory led to greatly increased slaughter, which was followed by a steady and alarming decrease in total numbers. As a result today the total population of both species of walrus is only a fraction of what it had been for centuries. It would be an exaggeration to say that either species is in imminent danger of extinction, but at the same time such reduction cannot be allowed to continue unchecked for much longer before real danger will threaten them.

For both species certain conservation measures have been put into force. The Danish Government, which controls most of the territory of the Atlantic walrus, has declared closed seasons when no walruses may be killed, and protected areas, and has further stipulated that walruses may only be killed by the native populations which depend upon them. The numbers which they are allowed to kill are related to their economic needs, and do not allow for excessive killing for ivory trading. Since many of the walruses are shot on ice-floes, which in the past has meant that only a minority of those shot have been recovered, the remainder sliding into the water, from which they could not be recovered, a new rule is now in force stipulating that no walrus may be shot until it has first been harpooned, a measure designed to prevent not only waste, but also the cruelty involved in the escape of seriously wounded animals.

The Canadian Government has adopted similar measures to regulate the killing of walruses in accordance with the needs of the Eskimo populations which depend upon them. The United States Wildlife Service is also examining the status of the Pacific walrus with a view to enforcing such measures.

The position of the walrus is somewhat different from that of the caribou. Both are primarily sources of food and other essential materials for native populations, and for these reasons it is imperative that both should be conserved, but whereas the decline of the caribou has been due entirely to wasteful killing following the advent of the rifle, and other factors concerned with the destruction of its environment, the walrus has suffered additionally from the discovery of the commercial value of its ivory. The caribou does not lend itself to commercial exploitation. Even so the commercial exploitation of the walrus has been in the main due to the native populations which depend upon it for other requirements. There has been no organised large scale commerical exploitation of the walrus by outsiders such as there has been of the fur seal and the sea otter which we shall consider later in the chapter.

Perhaps the most magnificent of all the larger Arctic animals is the polar bear, the second largest of all the world's carnivores, exceeded in size only by the giant brown Kodiak bears. It, too, is not subject to commercial exploitation on any large scale, but its present status is causing considerable anxiety for its eventual survival. The polar bear is completely circumpolar in its distribution, and consequently occurs as a native member of the fauna of all countries which embrace Arctic territory. These countries comprise Canada, Russia, Norway, Greenland (the responsibility of the Danish Government) and the U.S.A. with its Alaskan Arctic territory.

The polar bear, *Thalarctos maritimus*, is essentially a solitary creature of the pack ice. During the spring and summer it is carried southwards on the drifting ice-floes, but as autumn approaches it comes ashore and makes its way back northwards. Its food consists mainly of seals, many of which it catches as they come up through their breathing holes in the ice, or by stalking them across the ice. Stranded whales also attract them, and they seem able to detect the presence of a whale carcase from considerable distances. As many as forty full grown polar bears have been observed in the vicinity of a really big whale carcase.

The average weight of the males is about 1000 pounds, and of the females 600–700 lbs., although large males weighing more than 1600 lbs. have been recorded. Adult polar bears are in general solitary creatures. Males and females only come together for the short breeding season in the late spring. In the autumn pregnant females excavate a den for themselves in which they will remain throughout the winter. So far as is known they never come out to feed, relying upon the large stores of subcutaneous fat laid down while food is plentiful in the summer to tide them over until the following spring. While thus denned up they give birth to their cubs, usually one or two and occasionally three. Compared to their parents these are exceptionally small at birth, averaging only about two pounds. This small size seems to be an adaptation to the fact that until she finally comes out of her den in the early spring and begins to feed again the female has to provide not only all of her own food requirements but also those of her growing cubs from her own accumulated stocks. Large cubs would probably place too great a strain upon these stored resources.

Even so, by the time the cubs and their mother emerge from their partial hibernation they have grown to about 20 lbs. in weight. Parental care in polar bears is prolonged for a much longer time than it is in most other animals of comparable size. The cubs usually remain with her until the following spring, by which time they are half-grown and may weigh as much as 400 lbs. She is now ready to mate again, and either drives the cubs away or manages to give them the slip. Female polar bears thus produce young only every other year.

With the exception of man the polar bear is virtually without enemies, because no other Arctic animal is strong enough to attack it with any hope of success. Nor does it suffer in any way through destruction of its habitat. There is more than ample snow and ice to satisfy its territorial needs. If there is any reduction in its total population, only man can be blamed. In fact the present position of the polar bear is obscure. There is a strong feeling among experts that the total population is steadily decreasing, and that it may face the possibility of extinction in the near future, if indeed it is not already in danger. Despite all the efforts that have been made in the last few years to accumulate the necessary data, expert estimates of the present world population vary widely. The main reason for this is that it is such a nomadic animal, which may drift away on the ice-floes from one country in the spring, and land in another country when it leaves the floating ice in autumn, thus making it extremely difficult to get any kind of accurate estimate of the polar bear population of any particular country.

Like the walrus and the caribou, the polar bear plays an important part in the economy of certain Eskimo populations. Traditionally almost every part of the body was put to some use. The skin provided bedcovers, covers for sledges and leather for boots, and the flesh provided meat for both the Eskimos and their dogs, while the long canine teeth were valued as ornaments. Hunting for purely domestic needs, however, made no significant impact on the numbers. Recently, though, the rifle has given the Eskimos increased power over the bears, and a much greater toll has been taken. Skins were found to be a marketable product, and their sale gave an incentive to kill many more bears than were needed for the Eskimo's basic economy. Hunting by the personnel of the new air Arctic bases and meteorological stations is also growing steadily, and sealers have discovered that good money can be obtained by selling polar bear cubs, which can only be captured by shooting the mothers first.

Expert estimates of the present world population of polar bears vary from 18,000 from U.S.A. sources to something in excess of 5,000 from Russian scientists. The truth probably lies somewhere between these two figures. The Canadian estimate is in fact 10,000. Figures for the annual killings can be compiled more accurately, and at the present time it seems that rather more than one thousand bears are killed each year, more than half of them in Arctic Canada. If the American figures for the total number of bears are accurate, the population ought to be able to sustain a yearly loss of this order without any risk of diminution, but if the much lower Russian figure is anything like correct, then the species must be in urgent need of protection.

Precautionary measures which have already been taken to counteract any serious diminution in numbers also vary from country to country. The most important measures are undoubtedly those taken by the Russians. The 1955 General

Assembly of the International Union for the Protection of Nature recommended that all Arctic countries should take steps to protect polar bears, because lacking any precise data it seemed that this species was being subjected to very considerable pressure. In the following year the Russian Government responded to this appeal by issuing a special decree which banned completely the shooting of polar bears, and also imposed restrictions on the shooting of walruses and reindeer. In 1960 Wrangel Island, which contains one of the largest polar bear concentrations in the whole of the Arctic, was declared a polar bear reserve. During the autumn and winter, when the pregnant females are in hibernation, all forms of transport are prohibited on the island. As a result of these measures the Russian authorities estimate that the total number of polar bears in the Soviet Union has remained steady during recent years, and may even be increasing slowly. It seems therefore that even if the pressures on the polar bear populations in the rest of the Arctic prove to be more than the species is able to survive, ultimate extermination will certainly be averted by these timely Russian measures. Since 1956 the number of bears taken annually has been in the region of ten, and these have all been for zoos. Even allowing for a certain number of unauthorised killings, the annual crop is still negligible compared with the total Russian polar bear population.

In Canada, where the latest estimates give the number of polar bears killed annually as around six hundred, hunting is restricted to Eskimo populations dependent upon the bear for essential requirements. The polar bear population is also large and may well be able to sustain this rate of cropping without any steady reduction in its total numbers. In Alaska the last decade or so saw an alarming development in the methods of polar bear hunting with the introduction of the high-powered automatic rifle and the light aircraft. Such methods are now prohibited. Bona fide hunters using traditional methods are forbidden to kill cubs and females, and each is allowed only one male bear per year. For the privilege of killing it he has to pay a £50 licence fee. The native Eskimos are not restricted in the number of bears they may take, but they may only hunt them either on foot or by sledge. These measures, it is hoped, will ensure that the total yearly crop will be well within the polar bear population's capacity without any diminution in overall numbers.

In Greenland the resident population can kill bears without restriction, but no permits are issued to outsiders to hunt polar bears. In Norway the only limitation is that a foreign hunter is allowed to shoot only one bear.

Because of the lack of reliable information about the status of the polar bear, the U.S.A. Government called a conference of all nations in whose territory it lived. Delegates from the U.S.A., Canada, the Soviet Union, Denmark and Norway met in Fairbanks, Alaska, in September 1965. It was agreed that too little information was available to make it possible to formulate a joint policy for conserving the polar bear, and it was accordingly agreed that each country should initiate a programme of studies to find out as much as it could about the habits of the bear in its territory, and to formulate a more accurate estimate of its numbers than was at that time available. This work is now proceeding, and there seems every hope that since all the nations involved have expressed a strong desire to do all that they can to ensure the ultimate safety of the polar bear, a satisfactory future policy for its conservation can be anticipated with confidence as soon as the necessary data has been assembled.

The musk-ox, *Ovibos moschatus*, is another truly Arctic animal, completely adapted both in structure and habits to life on the windswept and tree-less tundra. Zoologically it is a particularly interesting animal, because although it looks very similar to a bison in general build, it in fact belongs to a small group of animals called goat-antelopes, which form a link between the true goats and the true antelopes. Until little more than a century ago it was common and widespread throughout the Arctic wastes of North America and Greenland, the total population in those days probably exceeding one million. Today it is doubtful whether as many as 20,000 survive.

Before considering the factors which led to this drastic reduction, and the attempts which are now being made to save the musk-ox from the threat of final extinction, we must take a look at the more important features of its structure and habits. Although smaller than the bison, the musk-ox has a similar general appearance. The massive horns meet in the midline above the eyes, forming a protective covering which no bullet can penetrate. Full-grown bulls weigh between five and eight hundredweight. Perhaps its most important feature, enabling it to withstand exposure to the Arctic winter, is its thick coat. This consists of an outer layer of long hair and a very thick inner layer of fine wool. On the shoulder the coat is particularly thick, and forms a distinct hump similar to that of the bison. The under-fur falls out in the spring, coming away in great wadding-like masses, which give the animal a very tattered appearance at this time. Before the onset of the next winter a new layer of under-fur will have grown to replace it.

For about three months the snow melts on the Arctic tundra, and for this short period the musk-oxen feed hard on the grass which springs up. Much of the food material in this grass is stored as a thick layer of fat beneath the skin, and will be used to eke out the very restricted food supplies which are available through the winter. These consist of lichens, mosses and dead grass, and to get at them the musk-oxen have to dig down with their feet. Because snow is always much less deep on steep slopes, the height of the winter sees the musk-ox foraging on the steep hill and mountain sides, exposed to the worst of the Arctic winds. It is then that they obtain full value from their wonderfully warm coats.

Apart from man the only natural enemy of the musk-ox is the wolf, against which they have evolved a defence system which would surely have won the approval of the Duke of Wellington had he known of it. On the appearance of a pack of wolves they never run away, but form up in a tight circle surrounding the calves, every individual facing outwards. Any wolf which is rash enough to attempt to drive home its attack usually finds itself lifted high in the air by a lightning thrust from a pair of horns, and as it falls to the ground may well be trampled to death beneath determined hoofs. Unless they realise the futility of their efforts fairly quickly and retreat, a group of bulls will suddenly break out of the circle and put them to flight.

The real onslaught by man on the musk-oxen herds only began in the 1870's. By this time he had virtually wiped out the enormous bison herds which only a few decades before had blackened the plains on their spring and autumn migratory journeys. Although of course their meat was valuable, the most important product of the bison slaughter was the skin, which formed a thick warm robe. As the supply of bison robes for travelling and bed rugs began to peter out, the hunters turned their attention to the musk-oxen, and discovered that even if they had to journey into the inhospitable Arctic to get them, their hides were even superior to the bison robes, and consequently fetched a price which made the hardship worth while. At about the same time the decimation of the Greenland herds also began, sealers and whalers shipping large regular consignments to Scandinavia, where their flesh was used either to feed dogs, or by fur trappers for bait. Their defence system, so effective against the wolf, made them an easy prey to the hunter's rifle. All he had to do was to set two or three of his dogs on the herd, which immediately took up its tight defensive circle, and shoot away. As one fell, so the others closed their ranks. Even when only a few remained alive, they would never attempt to escape, so that the complete herd was quickly annihilated.

The turn of the tide for the musk-ox began in 1930, when thirty-four young animals captured in Greenland were sent to Fairbanks in central Alaska, where they were at first kept in enclosures until they had become acclimatised. When they were eventually released they did not thrive as had been expected. A number of them were killed by bears. Also reindeer had recently been introduced, and seemed likely to be more useful to the Alaskan Eskimos than the musk-ox. In 1935, five years after their arrival, they were again captured and transferred to Nunivak Island off the Alaskan coast, where there were neither bears to prey upon them nor reindeer to compete with them for the very limited food supplies. Here they soon established themselves, and today there is a small but flourishing population.

Even under the most favourable conditions the musk-ox herds do not increase at a very spectacular rate. The females are believed to mate only every other year, and seldom have more than one calf. The mortality rate among the few calves which are produced is exceptionally high, probably because of the very harsh climate. Certainly it is known that in exceptionally severe winters when there is excessive snowfall large numbers of Greenland musk-oxen die of starvation, because the snow is too deep for them to be able to dig down to reach the meagre food supplies on which they depend to tide them over until the spring.

The turn of the century brought a new hazard to the continued existence of the musk-oxen. Sealers and whalers discovered that any musk-ox calves they could bring back alive found a ready sale to zoos, and provided them with a welcome additional income. Unfortunately, because of their natural defence system, already described, calves could only be captured after all the adults in the herd had been killed, thus wiping out the whole herd. It has been calculated that for every calf delivered to a zoo, bearing in mind that one herd might yield several calves, an average of six adults had been slaughtered. These were probably not put to any use, merely being left on the tundra for other animals to feed upon. Between 1900 and 1925 more than 250 calves are known to have reached zoos, and their capture must have made a significant contribution to the depletion of a world population which had already suffered severely at the hands of the nineteenth-century hunters. As soon as zoo directors realised how the calves were obtained they decided not to buy any more until a more economical method of capture had been devised.

Although they have survived on Nunivak, the hope that they would build up to a large population has not yet been realised, due to two factors. The native Eskimos began to shoot them before they had really had a chance to establish themselves, and they also found themselves in competition with large numbers of reindeer for the limited food supplies which the island is able to provide. Some time before the arrival of the musk-oxen, semi-domesticated reindeer had been introduced into the island. They did so well that by 1935 there were already too many of them, and the pasture was beginning to suffer from over-grazing. This led to an investigation sponsored by the U.S.A. Government, and in a report published in 1945 it was recommended that the reindeer herds should be drastically reduced. The Nunivak pastures, it suggested, could carry no more than 8,000 head of reindeer and up to 2,100 musk-oxen. The report has been accepted, and the reindeer have been drastically reduced. Latest reports confirm that the musk-oxen are steadily increasing.

Just over twenty years ago Professor John Teal, of Vermont University, U.S.A., began a series of experiments designed to return the musk-ox to Arctic regions as an important contribution to the economy of the people living there. In 1945, after making an intensive study of musk-oxen in the wild for several years, he conceived the idea of building up a domesticated herd on his farm in Vermont, in the extreme north-east of the U.S.A. not far from the Canadian border. The Canadian Government gave him permission to capture some calves provided he could do so without killing any of the adults. At first he tried netting them, but without success. He then hit upon a successful solution to his problem. He and his assistants chased a herd of musk-oxen into a lake, and as soon as they were swimming for the opposite shore he got into a canoe which had been hidden on the bank and followed them. When he caught up with a calf he jumped out of the canoe and roped it, his colleagues then helping him to carry it to the shore. Using this method he captured three calves in 1954 and another four in 1955. These were flown to his farm in Vermont to form the nucleus of his projected herd. The calves adjusted themselves very quickly to captivity, and in a few days became quite tame. One of the male calves grew into a magnificent bull weighing 1,400 lbs., by far the heaviest musk-ox ever recorded.

The calves, which were born during May and June, were weaned within three months. This left the cows free to mate again at the August rutting season, so that they bore a calf every year and not, as in the wild, every other year. In this way Professor Teal's herd increased much more rapidly than any wild herd.

The Arctic communities of Alaska and northern Canada are growing steadily and Professor Teal foresees the musk-ox becoming a most important domestic animal for these communities.

Although its flesh has always been described as unpalatable owing to its strong musky flavour, Professor Teal claims that the flesh of comparatively young domesticated animals has an excellent flavour similar to beef. The hide can be tanned to produce a very good quality leather, but the most valuable product of the musk-ox is likely to be its soft silky under-fur. When the animals moulted in May and June Teal found no difficulty in combing out the loose under-fur, which is one of the softest and silkiest of all natural fibres, even softer than the fine wool produced by the cashmere goat, and each musk-ox produces about six pounds of this *quiviut*, as the Eskimos call it, many times the amount of wool produced by one goat.

Professor Teal's work could have profound importance for the Eskimos and Indians living in Arctic North America. During the last few decades there has been a dramatic reduction of the caribou herds on which so many of them have always depended, and also a considerable decline in the numbers of seals and walruses, upon which they have also depended in varying degrees. Teal's idea is to provide them with domesticated musk-oxen herds to replace these wild animals, and thus make them less dependent upon the vagaries of wild species. Such herds would provide them with meat and leather for their own use, and large quantities of fine quality wool which could be used for commercial trading.

Having accumulated the necessary know-how for building up a domesticated herd of musk-oxen over a period of ten years, Professor Teal initiated the next stage in his plan to return the musk-ox to the Arctic in 1965. In that year he set up a herd on a farm near Fairbanks in Alaska with three dozen calves which he obtained from Nunivak Island. With the cooperation of the University of Alaska, his aim is to build up a musk-oxen bank, from which any Arctic inhabitants from Alaska to Greenland can be issued with a nucleus herd to establish their own musk-oxen ranch. Their only obligation is to return to the bank within seven years a number of calves equivalent to the animals with which they were originally issued.

Professor Teal has already had more than 1,500 inquiries for nucleus herds, but he estimates that it will be twenty years before the scheme is fully operational. It seems certain, though, that through his efforts the musk-ox will be safe from any further threat of extinction. Moreover its survival will also have made an extremely important contribution to the economy of the Arctic.

In contrast to the four species so far considered in this chapter the giant brown bears of Alaska and Kodiak Island have no commercial or economic value to the native populations, nor do they interfere with agriculture or any other human activity, yet they, too, have been facing considerable danger of ultimate extinction since before the end of the nineteenth century, through the utter selfishness of the big game hunter. Today the brown bear, *Ursus arctos*, is recognised as an extremely variable species having an almost complete circumpolar distribution, being represented in North America, Europe and Russia. At the beginning of the century experts divided the brown bears of the northern hemisphere into numbers of distinct species. One authority actually listed no fewer than eighty-four species and subspecies in North America alone!

Structurally, however, all brown bears are virtually identical, but they do differ very considerably in size, and on this basis several subspecies are recognised. The brown bears of Europe, for example, only weigh a few hundred pounds, and are the smallest of the species. The Kodiak bear, identified as *Ursus arctos middendorffi*, because it was first described by a Russian zoologist named Middendorf in 1851, is the largest of them all, though closely challenged by the bears of the nearby Alaskan mainland, which are today admitted to the same subspecies.

It was not until 1896, when the American naturalist Hart Merriam published a full description of the Kodiak bear, that the American big game hunter gave it his full and devastating attention. It was not only the largest bear in the world, but by far the largest carnivore, and as such merited greater attention from his rifle than almost any other living animal. To shoot a Kodiak bear became the proof that the hunter was in the premier class. This might not have mattered if he had been content to secure his trophy and return home with it. But having arrived at great personal expense, he regarded it as a great pity to leave without having slaughtered the largest possible number of bears, regardless of the fact that apart from his one trophy the remainder would be of little or no use to him. Such was the mentality of so many of the so-called sportsmen of the nineteenth and early twentieth centuries.

Thirty years after the publication of Merriam's description the species had been reduced to a remnant of its former numbers, and was seriously threatened with extinction. Fortunately the U.S.A. Government stepped in, and in 1926 the Kodiak bear was accorded complete protection. Since then its numbers have slowly recovered, but it still has to contend with unauthorised killing by the Eskimos.

We must now look at the histories of two sub-Arctic marine mammals which were brought to the brink of extinction by commercial exploitation—the fur seal, *Otaria ursina*, and the sea otter, *Enhydra lutris*. Neither of them is of any importance to native populations, but commercially they are of great value.

In 1741 the Russian explorer Vitus Bering led an expedition from Siberia to the hitherto unknown seas to the east. They discovered Alaska, but on their way home were shipwrecked on one of the group of islands now known as the Aleutian Islands, this one being subsequently named Bering Island. Bering, already seriously ill, soon died, but his colleagues set about the task of feeding themselves until the following spring, when they hoped to be able to construct some kind of vessel out of what was left of their own wrecked ship and make their way back home.

Searching for whatever animals they could find to provide them with the food they needed to avoid starvation, they discovered the sea otter living among the offshore seaweed beds and coming on to the shore rocks to rest. To them this sea beaver, as they called it, was principally a source of much needed food, but they did recognise that its pelt was thicker and softer than the pelt of any other animal then known.

By the following spring they had saved the pelts of eight hundred of these sea beavers whose flesh had played an important part in keeping them alive through the winter.

Many of the expedition had died, but the survivors managed to construct an improvised craft with which they succeeded in transporting themselves and the fabulous pelts back to Siberia.

The commercial possibilities of the sea otter were realised at once, and from then on the animal was hunted ruthlessly with no thought for its ultimate survival, but only for the vast immediate profits which it provided. As a logical consequence it was hunted to the verge of extinction. Indeed by the early years of this century it seemed certain that no sea otters survived. Nevertheless, just in case some small isolated population had managed to escape the ruthless exploitation of more than a century and a half, the American, Canadian, Russian and British governments signed a treaty in 1911 which accorded the sea otter absolute protection.

For more than twenty years, however, no evidence was forthcoming that any sea otters were in fact still in existence. Then, in the early 1930's, rumours began circulating that mysterious visits were being paid to one of the remote Aleutian Islands by Japanese fishing vessels, and that they were hunting a secret colony of sea otters. The American Government responded immediately by sending a naval vessel to investigate, and sure enough a colony of sea otters was discovered. Immediate steps were taken to give them all possible protection, and today the sea otter once again flourishes. It should only be a question of time before controlled exploitation can be allowed. This, as we have already emphasised, is the ideal aim for any animal species which has commercial value—conservation with controlled exploitation, and not just static preservation.

Before judging the Russian fur traders too harshly it must be remembered that before the days of central heating and closed cars the winter in Russia, and particularly in Siberia, was extremely severe, and warm furs were not a luxury, but a vital necessity. Whatever the consequences to the sea otters themselves, their pelts certainly played an important part in helping the Russians to survive the rigours of their bitter winter climate. The pity is that there was no realisation that provided the annual killings were related to the total population, the sea otter would have been able to produce a very considerable annual harvest without any serious reduction in the total population.

During the winter they spent on Bering Island Bering's men also discovered the fur seal. It did not live on the island, however, and only a few passing individuals were caught. There were enough to convince them that here was another animal whose pelt would be extremely valuable if it could be obtained in sufficient numbers. When the sea otter trade developed, efforts were made to track down the fur seals to their real home, but it was not until forty-five years after they were first sighted that their strongholds were discovered.

In 1786 another Russian explorer, Gerassim Pribilof, discovered the islands in the northern Bering Sea which now bear his name. And on the shores of these islands he found the greatest concentration of fur-bearing animals in the world. On the two islands of St George and St Paul millions of these creatures covered the beaches so thickly that scarcely any sand was visible between them.

Whereas it took about a century and a half to reduce the sea otter population to a position of near extinction, within thirty years of their discovery the fur seals of the Pribilof Islands had been almost wiped out. Their pelts had been gathered in unprecedented numbers in order to satisfy the appetites of the fur-hungry Russians.

In 1806 all killing of fur seals was halted for two years, after which the annual crop was much reduced. Even so by 1834 crisis again threatened the species. It was now that the Russian authorities formulated a plan which was to be the basis for all future successful attempts to conserve commercially valuable aquatic mammals from extinction. They decreed that in future only mature bulls should be killed, leaving the females to breed again and the pups to grow to full size. By the 1860's the total population had grown to between two and three million, and an annual crop of about 90,000 was being taken without any danger to the future of the species. When the U.S.A. bought Alaska and the various islands of the Bering Sea from the Russians in 1867 for the incredibly small sum of 7,200,000 dollars they adopted the same principles.

Towards the end of the century, however, crisis again faced the fur seal populations. By this time British and Canadian sealers had discovered that they could shoot the seals outside territorial limits as they made for their breeding territories in the Pribilof Islands. This was an extremely wasteful method, because many of those shot sank before they could be secured, and also because it was impossible to distinguish between males and females. In consequence as many females as males were killed, and each female shot meant also the loss of her pup, either as yet unborn, or left to starve on the beach where it had been deposited. It was not until 1911 that all the interested nations agreed to outlaw this method of pelagic sealing. Since then the fur seal population has steadily increased, so that today a commercial crop can be taken without endangering the species.

In addition to the sea otter and the fur seal, Bering's men also discovered a third aquatic mammal, the giant sea cow, or Steller's sea cow, named after the German zoologist who was a member of the expedition, and who subsequently published the only reliable description we have of this creature. Because it was easy to capture it provided a readily available source of meat for future fur traders, so that by 1770 it had become extinct. Its only other relatives are the manatees which live in the coastal waters and estuaries of Central America and the dugongs which live in the shallow coastal waters of east Africa, south-east Asia and northern Australia. These are both relatively small animals seldom exceeding six feet in length. The giant sea cow was twenty-five to thirty feet in length, and weighed up to four tons. After its extermination experts expressed doubts as to its ever having existed, and these were only dispelled in 1883 when an American zoologist, Dr Stejneger visited Bering Island and was able to collect some skeletons which fully confirmed both the former existence of the giant sea cow and its reported size.

Is there perhaps a possibility that Steller's sea cow still exists? In 1964 the crew of a Russian whaler reported seeing about six large animals which they could not identify in a part of the Bering Sea off the coast of Siberia which is still largely unexplored. Since 1800 there have been a number of reports of sightings of the giant sea cow in various parts of the northern Pacific, so perhaps it may eventually join the growing number of animals believed to be extinct which have been rediscovered in the last few decades.

Chapter 7

Birds on the Danger List

OF THE many thousands of bird species in the world a tiny minority are today faced with a considerable threat of extinction. Awareness of their predicament over the past decade or two has led to measures being taken to save them, so that today most of them are in a less vulnerable position than they were a decade or two ago. In this chapter we shall examine the present status of ten of the most important threatened species, and the measures which are being pursued in attempts to reinstate them.

The species which is perhaps having more attention lavished upon it than any other in order to rescue it from the threat of imminent extinction is the whooping crane of North America, *Grus americana*. This, one of the largest American birds, standing five feet high and having a wing span of seven and a half feet, has probably never been very plentiful. Since the last ice age there may never have been more than 1,500 individuals. Its reduction to a few dozen by the early years of this century was brought about through its choice of habitat for breeding, for it only nests in swamps. As settlement and civilisation expanded across the vast plains of Canada and the U.S.A., so flooded areas were drained and were replaced by crops, thus drastically reducing the areas available for whooping crane nesting sites. The related sandhill crane, which originally nested in similar territory, learned to use drier sites, but the whooping crane seemed to be incapable of making such a change.

By 1937 the total known population consisted of only a dozen or two pairs which spent the winter on the Texas coast of the Gulf of Mexico. In that year this coastal strip was established as the Aransas National Wildlife Refuge, and here the whooping crane was granted complete protection. Unfortunately, however, this is a migratory bird, and each year the whole population left its winter quarters to fly northwards to its summer breeding grounds, for no breeding ever took place at the Aransas Refuge. In the autumn the flock returned, together with the immature but by now well-grown young birds which had been hatched during the summer breeding season.

Despite strict protection on their winter grounds, the cranes did not recover their numbers as had been hoped. During the twelve years up to 1949 the largest number recorded at Aransas was only thirty-four. It seemed clear that until the summer breeding grounds had been discovered, and adequate protection introduced there as well, the chances of saving the species from extinction must remain remote.

As soon as the war ended the United States and Canadian governments instituted one of the most intensive bird hunts ever organised, designed to discover these winter breeding grounds. Nation-wide appeals were made by radio and through the press for any information which might lead to their discovery. Each year attempts were made to follow the migrating birds on their northward spring migration, but always somewhere en route they were lost. It was not until 1954 that the breeding grounds were finally discovered, in the far north-west of Canada, in the Wood Buffalo National Park. As the crow, or in this case the whooping crane, flies the distance between the summer breeding grounds and their winter quarters in the extreme south-east of the United States is all of 2,500 miles, a distance which the adult birds have to cover twice every year.

Although the Canadian nesting sites are probably too remote for the cranes to be in much danger during the nesting season, and at Aransas they are fully protected, they cannot be adequately protected during their lengthy migration flights. Much has been and is being done by way of propaganda to enlist the support of the public in doing all they can to ensure that these very rare birds come to no harm during these flights.

Even without human interference the task of building up their numbers is likely to prove very difficult for the cranes. A certain number of them are known to be killed by colliding with overhead power lines, but the most limiting factor is their slow rate of breeding. A normal clutch consists of only two eggs, and it is unusual for a female crane to rear more than one of the resulting chicks. The chicks are also susceptible to severe weather conditions, so that in some years hardly any of them survive. For these reasons the discovery of the breeding sites made no appreciable difference to the rate of increase of the flock. For example in 1949 the number of cranes wintering at Aransas was thirty-four, and fourteen years later, in the autumn of 1963, it was thirty-three. Since then there has been some improvement in the position. In 1965 forty-four birds turned up at the Texan wintering grounds, and in 1967 this number had increased by three to forty-seven. This must have been due to a particularly successful breeding season, because nine of the forty-seven were young birds of that year, which means that a number of adult birds were lost either on the breeding grounds or during the migration.

In view of the slow rate of increase of the wild flock the wildlife services of the United States and Canadian governments announced that plans had been made to set up a captive breeding programme. It was proposed to take one egg from each of six nests in a suitable year and attempt to incubate them. The eventual aim of this scheme would be to build up a nucleus flock in captivity from which adult birds could be returned to the wild to swell the existing flock, and even perhaps to build up additional flocks.

Up to that time only one pair of whooping cranes had ever been kept in captivity, and their breeding record was not very impressive. In 1940 an injured female was captured in Louisiana and taken to the Audubon Park Zoo in New Orleans. Subsequently a mate was obtained for her, and in 1945 she laid two eggs. One of these hatched, the chick having the distinction of being the first one hatched in captivity. After a few days it died. Not until eleven years later, in 1956, did the mother lay again. On this occasion two chicks were produced, but within a few weeks both of these had also died. Better fortune was achieved in 1957, when two chicks were hatched and reared to maturity, to be followed by another successful rearing in 1958. It was obvious, however, that much needed to be known about the requirements for breeding whooping cranes in captivity before this could become a regular established process.

It was accordingly decided that experiments in captive breeding would be conducted on the related but common sandhill crane. Some of the eggs taken from the nests were hatched in incubators and others under bantams. It was the success of these experiments which encouraged the authorities to go ahead with their plans for breeding whooping cranes in captivity in the 1967 nesting season. Six eggs, one from each of six nests, were taken and flown to the Patuxent Wildlife Research Centre in Colorado in portable incubators. As a result of this first experiment five chicks were reared successfully, and since, as already mentioned, nine young birds hatched and reared in the natural nesting grounds in the Wood Buffalo Park eventually found their way to the Aransas Refuge, it seems quite clear that the removal of the six eggs from the nesting grounds had no adverse effect upon the natural breeding on these grounds. In May 1968 ten eggs were taken from ten nests, and ten chicks were successfully reared. The captive flock, from which it is hoped eventually to reinforce the wild flock, is thus already fifteen strong after only two years.

By the early years of this century the American public had been made aware of the fact that they had allowed the American bison to become reduced almost to the point of extinction, and that the passenger pigeon, once the most numerous of all the birds in the North American continent, had been so decimated that it was probably already impossible to save it from extinction. The last known specimen in fact died, as we have seen, in 1914. In this new climate of public opinion a fresh look was taken at North American wildlife, in an attempt to discover whether any other species was likely to be faced with similar threats to its existence in the near future. The first species which obviously showed the need for active conservation measures was the trumpeter swan, *Cygnus buccinator*.

The trumpeter swan, like the whooping crane, is one of North America's largest birds. The only other North American swan, the smaller whistling swan, *Cygnus columbianus*, breeds only in the far north, and is so far in no danger. Until well into the eighteenth century the trumpeter swan was common throughout all western and central districts. As with the bison, it was the westward spread of civilisation, with its accompanying commercial exploitation which brought real danger to the species. Many birds were shot in the name of sport, but it was the discovery that the breast skins of the swans complete with their feathers could be sold in large numbers at great profit which really accounted for the wholesale slaughter and reduction of the species to a state of semi-annihilation.

By 1917 the position had become so serious that the Canadian and United States governments agreed upon a full-scale protection programme. All trade in breast skins was banned and all shooting forbidden. By 1930 the total population was estimated at about one hundred individuals. Today the species seems safe, the latest estimates giving a Canadian population of about seven hundred and a United States population of some four hundred birds.

But a new danger now threatens at least some of the trumpeter swan populations. Some of them live on lakes where wildfowl shooting is permitted, though of course not of the swans. Large quantities of spent lead shot find their way to the bottom of such lakes. Like other birds the swans require stones and gravel for the proper treatment of the food in their gizzards, and these they gather by diving to the bed of the lake, where they inevitably pick up some of the lead shot with them. This produces slow lead poisoning. Wildlife officers are now alert to the danger, and any birds obviously suffering from lead poisoning are caught and given stomach pump treatment to remove the shot, together with drugs to counteract any lead which may already have been absorbed into their systems.

A third North American bird which has fared much worse than the whooping crane and the trumpeter swan is the ivory-billed woodpecker, *Campephilus principalis*. A large bird, with a very distinctive black, white and scarlet plumage and white bill, it was at one time very common in many parts of the United States. It fed only on the various wood-boring grubs found in dead and dying trees. With the westward advance of civilisation and the consequent cutting down of forests the areas in which the woodpecker could survive were seriously and progressively reduced.

By the end of the last war it seemed that the ivory-billed woodpecker was virtually if not actually extinct. One single specimen seen by a Wildlife Service biologist in northern Louisiana in 1944 was the only sighting recorded for a number of years. In 1949 there were reports that a few had been seen in a remote forest area in Florida. This area was immediately declared a sanctuary, but further investigation failed to confirm the bird's presence.

As the years went by and no further sightings were reported the authorities became more and more convinced that final extinction had overtaken the species. In 1967, however, several pairs were discovered by an ornithologist working for the Bureau of Wildlife of eastern Texas. Active steps are being taken by the Bureau to negotiate agreement with the owners of the forests in the Neches River Valley, in which the birds are living, to protect sufficient trees for the needs of the birds. It is too early to say how many birds there may be in the valley, or what the chances of saving the species through this population might be. Every possible effort will of course be made to enable the bird to increase its numbers.

Those responsible for the attempts to build up a captive flock of whooping cranes have one encouraging example of the possibilities of captive breeding in the story of the Hawaiian goose over the past decade or so. The Hawaiian goose, *Branta sanvicensis*, or ne-ne, to give it its local name, is a relative of the European brent goose. Until the middle of the last century it was quite common on all the Hawaiian islands, with a total population of something like 2,500. Some time after this the numbers began to decline through a variety of causes. Many were shot to eat, and others were destroyed either as adults or as eggs and nestlings by cats, dogs, pigs and mongooses which had been introduced into the islands. As a result by 1950 the species was facing a grave threat of extinction. In that year the total population was estimated to be not more than fifty, and was still declining.

It was now that Peter Scott decided to attempt to establish a captive breeding flock at the Wildfowl Trust grounds at Slimbridge in Gloucestershire. Accordingly he managed to obtain two geese from Hawaii in 1950. These both turned out to be females, but in the following year a mate was obtained for them. In 1952 a total of nineteen eggs was laid, and from these nine goslings were successfully reared. Despite the rather low fertility, the flock grew steadily. By 1958 there were fifty-three birds at Slimbridge, and nine pairs had already been sent to other centres in Europe and the United States in order that other captive flocks might be established.

The most significant transfer from Slimbridge took place in 1962, when thirty birds were sent to the Hawaiian island of Maui. To protect them and their offspring from cats, dogs and pigs they were accommodated in a number of special fenced parks each about thirty acres in extent. The fences are eight feet high, sufficient to keep out their enemies, but allowing any that want to to fly out and establish themselves outside the parks. The success of the Slimbridge efforts can be gauged from the fact that the total world population is probably now at least four hundred, and is increasing steadily.

Another bird from the Pacific islands which has faced extinction during this century but now seems to be approaching safety is the Laysan teal, *Anas laysanensis*, a small duck which is found only on the one small island of Laysan, about 1,000 miles to the west of Honolulu. When it was first investigated by an expedition in 1911 it seemed to be on the very verge of extinction, for only six specimens could be found. Why it should have been so rare was a mystery, for it was not subject to human persecution, and did not seem to be under any great pressure from natural enemies. Over the next forty years, however, occasional visits to Laysan revealed that the teal still survived and was just about holding its own. In 1923 twenty teal were counted, and in 1936 eleven were seen. By 1950 the position seemed to have improved somewhat. The count for that year gave twenty-six adults and seven young.

From about this time the number of teal showed a sudden and

mysterious increase. A visit to the island in 1955 by the Director of the Pacific Oceanic Fisheries Investigations revealed the presence of at least 161 teal, and a second visit in 1957 found so many birds that it was impossible to give a reliable count, but it was estimated that there were not less than 580 adult birds on the island at that time. Large and expanding populations of any species bring their own anxieties, because these conditions can lead to overcrowding, and overcrowding in its turn can provide the ideal conditions for the outbreak and rapid spread of disease.

Since there was such a large population this seemed the right time to attempt to establish flocks elsewhere, which would ensure the survival of the species if epidemic disease wiped out the original wild population. In 1958, eighteen pairs were caught and distributed to various breeding centres in America and to the Wildfowl Trust. As a result small but flourishing breeding flocks of Laysan teal are now well established in a number of different places, and attempts are being made to release small groups on some other Pacific islands in the hope that additional wild populations may be established.

A flightless bird seems almost a contradiction, yet there have been and still are a number of well established birds which have completely lost the power of flight. Birds which are able to fly escape the attentions of rats and many other small predatory carnivorous mammals which would otherwise prey upon them. Even when they rest and nest they generally do so in trees where they are still out of reach of these potential enemies. The large flightless birds, the ostrich of Africa, the rhea of South America and the emus and cassowaries of Australasia are large and powerful enough to defend themselves against the native predatory mammals in the countries in which they live. In certain islands much smaller flightless birds have been evolved and have been able to flourish because there have been no small predators to menace them.

New Zealand is particularly rich in such small flightless birds, the most famous being the kiwi, which has become the national emblem of the country. Altogether there are five different species, one found on North Island, three on South Island and the fifth on Stewart Island. In earlier times kiwis were quite common. Many of them were killed to eat, and the Maoris used kiwi skins as an integral part of their ceremonial dress, but the populations were large enough to cope with these demands. It was the advent of the white settler which really exposed the kiwis to the danger of ultimate extinction. They were not themselves interested in the birds as a source of food, but they brought with them dogs, cats and ferrets, all of which found the kiwis particularly easy prey. And so their numbers decreased at a steady and alarming rate.

When the danger to their ultimate survival became obvious the New Zealand Government stepped in and accorded all kiwis absolute protection. Such measures can of course be enforced so far as human predators are concerned, but it takes more than legislation to protect an animal from its natural enemies, whether these be natives or introduced. To guard against the possibility that kiwis might become extinct despite all the efforts to save them, a centre was set up at Hawke's Bay where it was hoped they might breed. It was at this centre on 9 October 1946 that the first kiwi was bred in captivity, when a female chick was hatched. The present position is that small wild populations still survive, and the technique for breeding the birds in captivity is still being evolved. It seems reasonable to hope that the combined efforts at captive breeding and preservation in the wild may result in saving one of the world's most interesting birds from final extinction.

If we go north from New Zealand to Japan we find two conspicuous birds which are very near to extinction, and which are subject to every possible attempt at preservation. The Japanese crested ibis, *Nipponia nippon*, was at one time common and widely distributed not only throughout Japan but also in northern China, Manchuria and Korea. Today there may be a few survivors in the last three countries, though why they have suddenly become so scarce is a mystery. In Japan their drastic reduction to a mere remnant of their former numbers seems to be directly connected with forest clearance.

The Japanese ibis nests in trees, and the nesting tree must be surrounded by many others. Thus as trees are cut down any tree suitable for nesting is abandoned as it becomes isolated. The total Japanese population in 1967 was estimated to consist of one solitary bird on the Noto Peninsular and eight on Sado Island.

In a last desperate attempt to save the ibis plans have been announced for the establishment of an Ibis Preservation Centre, where attempts will be made to breed the birds under conditions of semi-captivity, provided that a nucleus stock can be obtained.

The case of the Japanese white stork, *Ciconia ciconia boyciana*, is a particularly interesting one. In 1958 it was reported to the International Council for Bird Preservation that only twenty-one birds remained. Four years later only thirteen birds were left, and none had bred for three years. The trouble seemed to be that although eggs were laid they did not hatch because they were infertile. There was good evidence that this in turn was due to contamination of their food by insecticides. A programme is now being carried out to capture the remaining storks and provide each pair with its own aviary in which uncontaminated food can be provided.

From Japan we travel to North Korea, the only country in which Tristram's woodpecker is known to have existed in recent times. In the Red Book it is described as 'extremely rare and may even be extinct.' In fact no reports of its continued existence had been received for a number of years, until in 1966 an expedition discovered two nests near Kaesong, one containing six young birds being fed by their parents, and the other five eggs. As soon as the expedition reported the North Korean Government responded by declaring the area in which the birds had been discovered a natural monument, and prohibiting any hunting or capture. The expedition gave its opinion that the total population of woodpeckers in the area might amount to several dozen. It is too early yet to estimate the birds' ultimate chances of survival.

Our tenth and last example of birds facing serious threats of extinction is not a single species but a whole group. The total number of bird species in the world runs into many thousands, and the relatively small number which are in danger occur haphazardly throughout the many groups into which birds as a whole are divided. But among the pheasants nearly one-third are listed as being in danger of extinction. Altogether forty-nine living species of pheasants are recognised, of which fifteen are causing anxiety. Pheasants are among the most colourful of all the world's birds. Besides the birds normally referred to as pheasants the group also includes the peafowl and the jungle fowl from which the domestic chicken is descended. With one exception, which lives in Africa, all pheasants come from southern and central Asia.

The common game pheasant, *Phasianus colchicus*, has been introduced into many parts of the world, and is now common in many parts of Europe. It is certainly never likely to find itself in any danger of extinction. Several other species are very popular as ornamental birds on large estates, notably Reeves's pheasant, Lady Amherst's pheasant and the golden pheasant, the latter now establishing itself also in Thetford Chase in Norfolk. The two species of peafowl, the Indian peacock and the green peacock, have for long been popular introductions into many parts of the world.

The inevitable question which arises in dealing with the pheasants is why so many species have become scarce. The main reason is that they are essentially birds of forests and woodlands, and the rapid increase in populations in Asia has led to widespread destruction of these habitats to make way for the necessary expansion in agriculture. For species which are common and widespread this destruction has only had a marginal effect on their total numbers. Many species, however, have always been extremely local in their distribution and limited in their numbers, so that if they become involved in any drastic reduction of habitat the effect on their prospects of survival can be extremely serious.

It was because of the increasingly desperate situation of so many of the world's pheasants that Philip Wayre founded the Ornamental Pheasant Trust at Great Witchingham in Norfolk in 1958, with Jean Delacour, the great French ornithologist and authority on pheasants, as its president. The aims of the Trust were to build up collections of as many of the rare pheasants as possible in an attempt to establish flourishing breeding stocks. Having done this it was hoped that it might eventually be possible to return stocks to their original habitats to augment depleted wild populations, or to replace those which had already disappeared. Today the Trust has the largest captive stocks of rare pheasants in the world, and a consignment of one species has already been returned to its native country.

Swinhoe's pheasant, *Lophura swinhoe*, is confined to the hill forests of Taiwan (formerly Formosa). In recent times it has become extremely scarce, but the trust has managed to build up a flourishing breeding group, and in 1966 it sent ten pairs to Taiwan, of which five pairs were released on Mount Alishan to join the remnant native population, while the other five pairs are to be maintained in captivity to produce others for release. The Taiwan authorities have declared Mount Alishan a national nature reserve in order to give the pheasants complete protection.

Chapter 8

Giant Tortoises and Marine Turtles: Have they a Future?

THE REPTILIAN order Chelonia, comprising the tortoises and the turtles, dates back at least 150 million years, making it one of the oldest surviving vertebrate groups. Despite its age, too, the order is by no means approaching its end. It still contains well over one hundred species, and many of these are widespread and flourishing. The largest members of the group, the giant land tortoises and the marine turtles, are, however, facing serious threats to their continued existence.

Until a few million years ago various species of giant tortoises were widespread and quite common in many of the warmer parts of Asia, Africa and America. Their extinction in comparatively recent times was probably due to the activities of newly-evolved mammal predators, which left survivors only in certain groups of islands in the Pacific and Indian Oceans. When first discovered in these islands in the sixteenth century these isolated populations were flourishing, but through ruthless exploitation many of them have been exterminated and the others reduced to danger level. Although so widely separated geographically the histories of the Indian Ocean and Pacific giant tortoises have been very similar.

In 1535 a Spanish explorer, Fray Tomas de Berlanga, discovered a group of islands in the Pacific Ocean some six hundred miles west of the coast of Ecuador. The most striking feature of these barren volcanic islands was the enormous number of giant tortoises which he found there. Indeed he named the group the Galapagos Islands, *galapagos* being the Spanish word for tortoise.

At first sight giant tortoises would not seem to be very useful animals commercially or in any other way. Unfortunately for their future, however, it was soon discovered that their meat was extremely palatable. So the Galapagos Islands became a regular port of call for mariners crossing the Pacific. An early writer described them as being 'extraordinarily large and fat, and so sweet that no pullet eats more pleasantly.'

In the days before refrigeration, when salt pork was about the only meat that it was possible to carry on a long voyage, these giant tortoises were found to have one great advantage, which was unfortunate for their own future. Provided they were kept below deck away from the sun, and their shells were not damaged, they could be kept alive and in good condition for many months without needing to be fed, and so were a means of providing a crew with fresh meat at all times.

Despite the enormous numbers which must have been taken over the intervening centuries, the giant tortoises were still plentiful when Darwin visited the Galapagos Islands during the famous voyage of the *Beagle* in 1835. This visit was perhaps the most epoch-making ever made by any naturalist anywhere, for the evidence which the islands provided enabled him to crystallise his ideas for his great theory of evolution.

By this time the pressure on the giant tortoise populations from the mariners was passing, but a new danger was already well established. By the turn of the century it had been discovered that the fat from a full-grown specimen would yield as much as three gallons of clear high-grade oil. This led to a further onslaught on the tortoises. By the end of the nineteenth century the position of the Galapagos tortoises was precarious. How many tortoises had been collected from the islands since their original discovery it is quite impossible to compute with any degree of accuracy. Estimates range from many hundreds of thousands to as many as ten millions, and the truth probably lies between these limits. To have withstood such rates of depredation their original numbers must have been very great indeed.

As though these two waves of intense exploitation were not enough, during the nineteenth century the islands were inhabited by small groups of colonists whose direct effect upon the tortoise populations was minimal. They probably took a few for food, but their requirements could easily be met without endangering the future. The danger they did introduce came from the animals they brought with them. Goats and pigs escaped from their farms and set up wild populations, the pigs competing directly with the tortoises by killing and eating them, and the goats indirectly by consuming the vegetation on which they relied for their food. Cats, dogs, mice and rats also presented their own threats to the tortoises.

Until very recently no one had known the true position of the various kinds of Galapagos tortoises. The Government of Ecuador, which owns the islands, had passed excellent laws to protect them, but to apply them had proved difficult. In 1959, however, the Charles Darwin Foundation for the Galapagos Islands was formed at an international meeting in Brussels. Its function was to ensure the continued survival of the unique fauna of the islands. The first task of the Foundation was to investigate fully the position of the tortoises, and to initiate measures for their preservation.

A full report published in 1964 revealed that the position was not quite as desperate as had been feared. Of the fourteen distinct types of tortoises which are known to have inhabited the islands in the past only two or three could definitely be recorded as extinct. However, as expected, the main danger to the remainder was the introduced animals, and of these the goats constituted the greatest menace. A concentrated programme to rid the worst infested islands of goats is now well under way. The first island to be tackled was Barrington, where the goat menace seemed to be worse than anywhere else. In June 1964 five men spent four days shooting them. In that time they killed two hundred and ten goats, and planned to return later to kill the one hundred or so which they estimated still remained. A month later they returned, and killed at least three hundred more! This systematic extermination of the goats will continue until they have been eliminated.

Although most of the tortoises exist today in small numbers,

Indefatigable Island still contains a large population estimated at about two thousand. Even they, however, are subject to certain pressures. There is quite a large farming population, and both farmers and fishermen take their toll of the tortoises. The Darwin Research Station has set up a reserve in part of the island where the greatest numbers are found. No tortoises may, of course, be taken in the reserve, and entry can only be obtained by special permit. Pigs, which prey upon the young tortoises, are being shot. Complete extermination will probably not be possible, but it is hoped that their numbers can be kept sufficiently in check to allow at least a proportion of the young tortoises to survive.

How many of the Galapagos Islands can retain their tortoises it is of course much too early to say. Certainly some of them should be safe, and none will be allowed to disappear without the utmost efforts being made on their behalf. With their long potential life, even a small population, if all the dangers threatening it were removed, might well stage a dramatic recovery.

At the time of their discovery the Indian Ocean giant tortoises were still living in at least thirty different islands in the western Indian Ocean including the Seychelles, Mascarene and Aldabra groups. Their initial discovery is not documented, but it occurred at about the same time as the discovery of the Galapagos tortoises. Their value as food, too, was as promptly realised, and they were taken from the islands without thought for the future of the species. Some idea of the numbers taken at the height of their popularity can be gained from the fact that during a period of eighteen months in the years 1759–60 some 30,000 were taken from the one island of Rodriguez.

By the middle of the last century the tortoises had become extinct in nearly all the islands except the Aldabra group. Today it is only in this group that the Indian Ocean giant tortoise still exists as a genuine wild animal. A certain number can now be found on some of the other islands, notably the Seychelles group, but these have all been imported during the past century from Aldabra to replace their lost populations.

The survival of the Aldabra tortoises was due to the fact that the Aldabra atoll was an inhospitable group of islands well away from any shipping lanes, and offering no commercial inducements. It would not have been worth while to go there for the tortoises alone.

Even during the 1950's little was known about the status of the Aldabra tortoises. Indeed it was reported that only small numbers remained, their reduction having been caused by large numbers of goats destroying the vegetation on which they lived. In order to investigate the present position of the tortoises, and also the fauna of Aldabra as a whole, the Bristol University Seychelles Expedition of 1964–5 spent two months there.

Aldabra is a coral atoll consisting of four islands surrounding a lagoon. To the surprise of the members of the expedition they found the giant tortoises extremely abundant on South Island, the largest of the four. In fact they estimated the total population of this island to be about 30,000, with about another 3,000 shared between North and Settlement Islands. Contrary to earlier reports there were only a few goats, capable of offering little competition to the vast numbers of tortoises.

A subsequent expedition to Aldabra undertaken by the Royal Society in 1967–8 revealed an even more favourable situation. Although any accurate count was impossible because of the vast numbers, it was certainly established that the numbers of tortoises was not less than 60,000 and might be as high as 100,000.

Besides discovering the only really large giant tortoise population left in the world today, the Bristol expedition were also able to reveal a living museum of natural history as interesting and important as that of the Galapagos Islands. It is sincerely to be hoped that Aldabra, too, may become a centre for natural history research.

World opinion was shocked in 1966 when the British Government proposed to construct an air base and a radio station on South Island. Conservation bodies in all parts of the world protested, because such a move would result in the extermination not only of the tortoises, but of many birds and other animals unique to the atoll. Like the Galapagos Islands, Aldabra has its own peculiar species and subspecies. The two groups of islands in fact probably constitute the two finest areas left in the world for the intensive study of evolution. The Galapagos Islands have been saved for research, and one must hope that a complementary organisation can be established at Aldabra.

Fortunately the devaluation of the pound towards the end of 1967 caused the British Government to shelve its plans for Aldabra, and it seems extremely unlikely that they will ever be revived.

Giant tortoises are vegetarian, and are able to exist on very poor quality material. On some of the Galapagos Islands there is little else for them to eat but coarse grasses and cacti, and water is often scarce. Darwin described the regular journeys made by them in search of water. 'The tortoise is very fond of water, drinking large quantities, and wallowing in the mud. The larger islands alone possess springs, and these are always situated towards the central parts, and at a considerable height. The tortoises, therefore, which frequent the lower districts, when thirsty, are obliged to travel from a long distance. Hence, broad and well-trodden paths branch off in every direction from the wells down to the sea coast; and the Spaniards, by following them up, first discovered the watering-places. When I landed at Chatham Island, I could not imagine what animal travelled so methodically along well-chosen tracks. Near the springs it was a curious spectacle to behold many of these huge creatures, one set eagerly travelling onwards with outstretched necks, and another set returning after having drunk their fill. When the tortoise arrives at the spring, quite regardless of any spectator, he buries his head in the water above his eyes, and greedily swallows great mouthfulls, at the rate of about ten a minute.'

It seems certain that giant tortoises can live for at least one hundred years. Large specimens can certainly weigh more than 600 lbs., for London Zoo has had a specimen of this weight on exhibition. The maximum possible weight may well be in excess of 800 lbs. A large individual is not necessarily very old. Given plenty of food and warm temperatures a tortoise can reach giant size in about twenty years from hatching. After this it will continue to grow throughout its life, but of course much more slowly.

Despite their size, these tortoises are not the largest living chelonians. This distinction belongs to the leathery turtle, *Dermochelys coriacea*, which is found in many of the tropical and sub-tropical seas of the world. Occasional specimens in fact occur well away from their normal range, one specimen weighing about five hundredweight having been landed by fishermen at White-haven in England in 1960. On the advice of the local officer of the R.S.P.C.A. it was subsequently returned to the sea.

To the preservationist the leathery turtle is a particularly interesting animal. Its flesh is generally considered to be unpalatable, and no one hunts it. Nor, so far as is known, is it preyed upon by any other marine animals. Yet it is in imminent danger of extinction because its eggs are considered a delicacy, and since they are laid on beaches they are readily accessible to the professional egg collector. During the past few years, as we shall see, determined efforts have been made to ensure that at least a small proportion of the eggs shall be allowed to develop in order to maintain the population.

Unlike all other marine turtles the leathery turtle lacks a true shell. Instead it has a thick leathery skin in which are embedded a number of separate bony plates. Full grown specimens attain a length of about six feet and a weight of at least half a ton. Specimens approaching three quarters of a ton in weight have in fact been reported. Like all turtles its limbs are modified as swimming paddles.

Although it spends virtually all its life at sea, feeding on all kinds of small animal life, it is still dependent upon land for breeding. At the breeding season the fertilised females swim ashore on a suitable sandy beach, haul themselves slowly up until they reach the high tide mark, and then proceed to dig a hole about three feet deep. Into this hole the female lays between one hundred and one hundred and twenty eggs, and after carefully filling it in she returns to the sea. During the breeding season she will make between five and ten of these egg-laying visits.

In about two months the eggs hatch, and by a concerted effort many of the small turtles produced in each nest are able to make their way to the surface. Instinct takes them down the beach towards the sea, but many of them never reach the water. Flocks of sea-birds and hordes of crabs attack them, so that only a small proportion of those which emerge successfully from the nests reach the safety of the sea. And even this is not real safety, for as they swim out across the inshore waters many more of these baby turtles are captured and eaten by all kinds of fish and other animals which inhabit these waters. In the event only a very tiny percentage of the turtles which hatch actually manage to get as far as a quarter of a mile from the shore. Once they do achieve this, they are much less vulnerable to attack, an important fact in the present conservation attempts, as we shall see.

Thus without any interference from man the leathery turtle faces almost overwhelming natural odds against it. Add to this the fact that for some time past until very recently all the eggs from every nest which could be found were dug up and sold for food, and it will be obvious why the future survival of the leathery turtle has become an extremely urgent conservation problem.

Until 1952 the only known nesting sites of the leathery turtle were on certain beaches in Ceylon and Costa Rica, with occasional landings also reported from India and the mainland of North America. It was realised, however, that the small numbers of females coming ashore at these nesting sites represented only a small proportion of the world population, and that therefore the main nesting sites still remained to be discovered.

This vital discovery took place in 1952, when the turtle was found to come ashore to breed on a $7\frac{1}{2}$-mile beach at Trengganu in Malaya. It soon became apparent that this was by far the most extensive nesting beach for the leathery turtle, and on subsequent calculations it is believed that between 85 per cent and 95 per cent of all the female leathery turtles in the world haul out on this one short stretch of coastline to lay their eggs. So whatever conservation measures may be adopted on other beaches where the turtle is known to breed, its eventual survival must depend mainly upon the success of whatever efforts are made at Trengganu.

Prior to this general discovery the inhabitants of the Trengganu region had known of the turtle landings, and had taken their annual toll of the eggs. Now, however, the Malayan Government stepped in and put turtle egg collecting on a proper commercial footing. The beach was divided into a number of sections, and each section was leased on an annual basis to the collector who submitted the highest bid for the licence. This procedure had a devastating effect upon the nests. When a collector had paid perhaps as much as £4,000 for the privilege of collecting eggs which he could then sell for the equivalent of twopence each, it was essential to him to collect all the eggs from every nest he was able to uncover. The terms of his licence, unfortunately, did not require him to leave any eggs in the nests to hatch.

The danger of allowing virtual complete removal of all eggs laid was soon realised by Professor Hendrickson of the University of Malaya, and the Malayan Nature Society. They put forward a scheme by which the eggs from a proportion of the nests should be dug up and reburied in a special enclosure on the beach. A strong fence would prevent other turtles digging up these nests, and would also discourage predators. As they hatched, it was proposed that the young turtles should be collected up and kept for about a week, after which they would be released into the sea a few hundred yards offshore. This would mean that they had been protected from many of the initial hazards. Although no precise figures are available, there is reasonable evidence that of every thousand eggs which hatch only one hundred and twenty-five young turtles survive for more than one week. It must also be remembered that many eggs are dug up and eaten by predators even before they have had a chance to hatch. Thus every thousand young turtles released from the hatchery represent something like 8,000 turtles hatching and reaching the surface of the sand in the normal way.

With a grant of 2,000 Malayan dollars the Malayan Nature Society was able to organise and stock its first hatchery with about 8,500 eggs, from which 3,700 young turtles emerged on the surface. The discrepancy was accounted for by the fact that quite a high proportion of eggs proved infertile, and many of those which did hatch were unable to dig themselves up to the surface. Subsequent years have seen a much higher proportion of successful emergence. In 1965, for example, 7,200 turtles were released into the sea from 9,600 eggs buried in the hatchery. Attempts have been made over the past few years to mark the young turtles, in the hope that they can be recognised when they will be able to tell us more about a particularly interesting animal about which little is really known.

Stimulated by the efforts being made in Malaya, the Ceylon Wildlife Department have also been operating a hatchery for leathery turtles since 1962, though on a much smaller scale.

The present position of the leathery turtle seems to be that the total world population numbers something in excess of one thousand pairs, of which the vast majority belong to the group which nest in Malaya. Now that the urgency has been realised it must be hoped that the measures just described will be sufficient to avert final extinction. Given adequate hatching, there would seem to be no reason why local cropping of the eggs should not continue. The immediate aim must be to find out how many young turtles need to be released from the hatcheries each year in order to maintain the total world population.

In 1965 it was discovered that a small number of leathery turtles were coming ashore on the coast of Natal to lay their eggs, and efforts are being made by the Natal National Parks Board to have an area of beach set aside as a sanctuary during the breeding season. In this way it is hoped that the turtle population represented by these nesting females may gradually increase in size. Little is really known about the general biology and habits of the turtles, but it does seem possible that if increases in numbers of those groups already known can be effected, then some turtles might choose new beaches for egg-laying. For an animal whose world total is so small, the more separate groups there are the more likely is the species to be able to survive.

Altogether there are six different species of marine turtles, but the other five differ from the leathery turtle in possessing a complete shell like that of a typical land tortoise. Their habits, however, are all more or less similar. They are all completely aquatic, living in tropical and subtropical waters, and lay their eggs on sandy beaches. The males, so far as is known, never haul out of the water.

The green or edible turtle, *Chelonia mydas*, is also in need of urgent protection if it is to escape the present threat of extinction. Whereas the leathery turtle is endangered by purely local exploitation, the commercial value of the green turtle is virtually worldwide, for it is from its flesh that turtle soup is made. Small numbers of green turtles are caught and eaten by primitive peoples, but the vast majority killed find their way to the capitals of the world to be served up at leading banquets.

Very little is really known about the total world population, except that it has been diminishing at an alarming rate over the past few decades. In recent times as many as 1,200 frozen carcases have been imported into London in a single year, while New York in a similar period has received as many as 20,000 live specimens, most of which would be used to produce canned turtle soup for sale in chain stores and supermarkets. That the existing population cannot support exploitation on this scale for long is certain. It has in fact already disappeared or become rare in many areas where it was formerly abundant.

The best hope for the eventual safety of the species lies in the efforts being made in Borneo under the direction of Tom Harrisson, Curator of the Sarawak Museum. In almost every part of the world where it has occurred the edible turtle has always been killed for food. In Thailand, Malaya, Indonesia, Borneo and the southern Philippines, however, for reasons which are variously religious or traditional, killing the turtles has always been taboo, though their eggs have been collected. Like those of the leathery turtle, they are considered a luxury, and are in fact of high grade food value.

The nesting beaches are not on the mainland, but on three small islands off the south-western tip of Borneo. In 1947 the management of the turtles and their eggs was handed over to Tom Harrisson as an extra duty. His work since then as Executive Officer of the Turtles Board has fallen under three headings: he has been responsible for the annual collection and sale of eggs, for the initiation and development of a comprehensive hatching and rearing programme, and for a research programme designed to find out more than the little that was hitherto known about the habits of the green turtle.

The peak egg-laying period is from July to September, and during this time a constant watch is kept on the beaches. As soon as a clutch has been laid and covered up, a small marker flag is placed over it, so that it can be located subsequently. All marine turtles cover up their nests so skilfully that it is usually quite impossible to see where they have been excavated. When they are dug up, those which are to be sold are taken to the mainland by launch, where they are sold wholesale at a price equivalent to about threepence each. Something approaching a million eggs are sold each year.

The Turtles Board does not get a government grant, the money needed to finance the hatchery and research programme coming out of the proceeds of the egg sales. In the early days the percentage of the hatchery eggs producing young turtles was low, but as knowledge and techniques improved, so the percentage gradually increased. Today about 70 per cent of all the eggs laid down in the enclosed hatchery do produce turtles, and the majority of these are then successfully reared for a few weeks while their shells harden. Only then are they taken out to sea and released. The number of eggs put down each year is now something like 100,000 or 10 per cent of the total number deposited on the beaches, and this means that some 60,000 young turtles are subsequently released.

Although not so large as the leathery turtle, the green turtle is nevertheless a large animal. 250 lbs. is considered quite a good adult today, but exceptionally large specimens are known to turn the scales at as much as 850 lbs. The average clutch size is something over one hundred, similar therefore to that of the leathery turtle, as is the incubation period of between fifty-two and sixty days, depending upon beach and weather conditions. Tagging has shown that each female turtle normally lays more than once in a season, some in fact making as many as eight separate landings, the interval between one landing and the next being nine to twelve days. If the first visit of the year is made to a certain beach, all subsequent visits will almost invariably be to the same beach.

After one season of egg laying a turtle generally disappears completely for at least three years. Similar tagging experiments with green turtles in the Caribbean have shown that they, too, do not return to breed every year, though some do return after two years. Little is known about what happens to the turtles during their long years at sea. Only one of the large number tagged has ever been recovered other than on its return to the beaches, but it is hoped that continued investigation may eventually reveal a great deal more information about the life of the turtles. Equally mysterious is the virtually complete disappearance of the young turtles after their release. Very few have ever been seen either in the Indian or Pacific Oceans. Where their growing up takes place is just not known. Lack of this knowledge of the habits of the young and the adults makes it difficult to formulate an adequate conservation plan.

Apart from these Borneo turtles, there is only one other population which is now being afforded protection. In earlier times green turtles existed in enormous numbers in the Caribbean, coming ashore on many of the islands to breed. Today they have been all but wiped out. Through the efforts of Professor Archie Carr, however, one of the last remaining nesting beaches has now become the second world sanctuary for the green turtle. In 1963 the Government of Costa Rica prohibited all further exploitation of the green turtles using the nesting beach at Tortuguero. Apart from the danger to the species of continued uncontrolled exploitation of the turtles, the methods used to capture and transport them alive involve very considerable cruelty.

All is not of course lost. It is to be hoped that these protective measures in Borneo and Costa Rica will prove effective, enabling the turtle populations not only to hold their own but to increase steadily. There are also other populations in other parts of the world. In the Seychelles and the other island groups of the Indian Ocean green turtles used to be extremely abundant, and were an important source of food for the local populations. Their position today is precarious, and any long-term improvement here will have to include persuading these local populations that it is in their interests to limit the numbers of turtles they take each year, a very difficult task when the people concerned are only semi-literate.

The only other turtle which has any commercial value is the hawksbill turtle, *Eretmochelys imbricata*, whose shell provides the tortoiseshell of commerce. For some time after the introduction of plastics much of the pressure was removed from this turtle. Real tortoiseshell of good quality was always expensive, and imitations made from plastics were very much cheaper. Now, however, the demand for tortoiseshell is again increasing, and the position will have to be watched very carefully.

Chapter 9

Rediscoveries and possible New Discoveries

So far in this survey we have considered the problems of saving from possible extinction animal species already well known to science. In this last chapter we shall consider the prospects of animals not yet discovered, or animals believed to be already extinct which may be or have recently been rediscovered. The idea that all animal species, apart from some obscure insects and other small kinds, are already known, and that no more remain to be discovered, is quite erroneous.

Quite a number of mammals and birds have been rediscovered during the past few decades long after they were believed to have become extinct, and at least one mammal species has been discovered for the first time in the same period. Such discoveries really test the efficacy of our preservation methods. If a sizeable animal can have remained undiscovered or at least have apparently vanished for many decades after its initial discovery, it is clearly either a very rare species, or a species with a very limited distribution. In either case the sudden release of information of its existence and whereabouts could well result in its rapid final extinction if it was pursued by collectors before adequate safeguards for its protection could be devised.

Perhaps the best example of rediscovery is that of the takahe, a New Zealand bird belonging to the rail family. The story of its initial discovery begins in 1847, when W. Mantell, a government official interested in natural history, unearthed the bones of a strange bird among volcanic ash. Unable to identify these remains, Mantell sent them to the great British anatomist Sir Richard Owen, who decided they belonged to a hitherto unknown species, which he accordingly named *Notornis mantelli* as a compliment to its discoverer.

For the next two years, when official duties allowed, Mantell continued the search for further relics of the apparently extinct bird. Finally, in 1849 he was rewarded, not with the discovery of more bones, but with the skin from a recently caught specimen. Some sealers had caught the bird and eaten it, and Mantell came up with them before they had had time to dispose of its skin. Some little time later a group of Maoris captured a live specimen, and this also found its way into Mantell's hand. Both specimens were sent to the British Museum, where for the next thirty years they remained as the only tangible evidence of the existence of the species, for nothing more was heard of Notornis until 1879. In that year a third specimen was caught by a dog whose owner was out catching rabbits near Lake Te Anau, at the southern end of South Island. This specimen was preserved and sent to London, where it was auctioned and bought by a representative of the Dresden Museum for one hundred guineas. The fourth specimen was also caught by a dog in the same area in 1898. The two men who were camping on the shores of the lake with the dog at once realised that they had obtained something of exceptional interest, and they sent it at once to Invercargill. Examination showed it to be the best of the only four specimens of Notornis yet found, and it was purchased on behalf of the New Zealand Government for £250 to prevent it going abroad, and deposited in the Dunedin Museum.

For the next fifty years the takahe seemed to vanish again, except for occasional reports that it had been seen for a moment or heard in the same region from which the last two specimens had been obtained. In the 1920's at least one of these reports seemed sufficiently reliable to suggest that the bird did still exist, and on the strength of this the New Zealand Government granted it absolute protection just in case it should reappear.

The final rediscovery of the species was achieved in 1948 by Dr C. B. Orbel during an intensive search for it in a remote valley situated between 2,000 and 3,000 feet above sea-level in the mountains to the west of Lake Te Anau. As soon as the news was announced the government declared the whole valley a sanctuary. The four earlier specimens had all been taken within a twenty-mile radius of this valley.

The takahe is a heavily-built bird about the size of a full-grown domestic hen, which is large for a rail. It is quite brightly coloured, with an iridescent breast, turquoise back and wings, and scarlet legs and beak, the latter being short and very thick. The adults seem to feed exclusively on tussock grass, which abounds in Takahe Valley and in the few neighbouring valleys in which it is now also known to live. For a nest it constructs a bowl of this grass in the middle of a tussock presumably to protect it from the weather and from its enemies. One or two eggs are laid, and the young chicks which hatch after an incubation period of four weeks are fed on insect pupae and worms until they are about two months old, when they change over to a vegetarian diet.

The future prospects for the takahe are not very bright, despite all the efforts which have been made. Breeding in the wild is very dependent upon the weather which is sometimes so bad during the breeding season that no chicks are hatched. Not only are the clutches small, but the percentage of fertility is also low. The major threat, however, comes from the large herds of red deer and wapiti which unless drastically controlled may well destroy the natural vegetation on which the birds are completely dependent. Even the attempts which have so far been made to establish breeding colonies in captivity have not met with any significant success. Clearly much more needs to be known about the bird's requirements in captivity before there can be much hope that this method can be looked to to save the species.

The takahe, as already indicated, is certainly not the only example of an animal believed to be extinct which has turned up again in recent years, and it would be a rash assumption to suppose that future years will not add to their number. By the same token we may well expect hitherto unknown species to be discovered for the first time.

On 17th December 1961, a Western Australian naturalist named Harley Webster was enjoying a day's fishing along a lonely creek when he heard the call of a bird which he had certainly never heard before. Although it seemed incredible, it sounded to him very like the description he had read of the song of the noisy scrub bird, *Atrichornis clamosus*, a bird which had been known in parts of Western Australia during the nineteenth century, but which had not been reported by anyone for about fifty years, and had therefore been assumed to have become extinct. Its remarkable rediscovery was announced in the Press on Christmas Day. Since then great efforts have been made to provide an area which can be designated a sanctuary where the noisy scrub bird can live unmolested in its native habitat.

At the time of writing the most recent rediscovery is that of a small Australian mammal known as the dibbler, *Antechinus apicalis*. In January 1967 Michael Morcombe, an Australian naturalist, was endeavouring to capture specimens of the tiny honey opossum near the Waychinicup River to the east of Albany in Western Australia. These little marsupials are specially adapted with slender muzzles for feeding on nectar. Morcombe was using small cages which fitted over the large banksia flowers which the animals are known to visit, the idea being that when they came to the flowers during the night they would touch a trip wire which would close the cage while they were within it. For three weeks the search went on, but not a single animal was captured. Then at last success came. But the two captives which were finally obtained were not honey opossums but dibblers. One can imagine the naturalist's surprise to be in possession of two specimens of a mammal which had last been seen eighty-three years before, and which by now had been assumed to have become extinct some time during the intervening period. Two months later a third specimen was captured. Already one of the specimens has given birth to eight young. Efforts are now being made to find a suitable area in which the dibbler still exists and can be preserved.

Only a few months before the rediscovery of the dibbler an even more unusual discovery was made in New South Wales of another marsupial mammal which had hitherto been thought to have become extinct at least twenty thousand years ago. In 1896 Robert Broom came across the fossilised remains of a small marsupial which he named *Burramys parvus*. For seventy years *Burramys* was regarded as just one of the many extinct marsupials which inhabited Australia long before man himself was evolved.

In August 1966, however, its status suddenly changed when a small opossum was captured by Dr Shortman in a ski lodge in the Victorian Alps about one hundred and thirty miles from Melbourne. Realising that the little creature was unusual, and being himself quite unable to identify it, he took it to the experts at the Victorian Fisheries and Wildlife Department. Much to everyone's amazement it turned out to be a male *Burramys*. Apart from the fact that the gap between its supposed extinction and its actual discovery as a living animal was nothing like so great, here was another Coelacanth story, involving this time a land and not a marine animal. Since the discovery of this single specimen the search for others has been going on, so far without success, but with the knowledge that they must be around somewhere.

We turn now to a bird the evidence for whose existence rests upon the discovery of only four specimens. In July 1905 an explorer-naturalist named Owston was making a collection of birds in the Shensi Province of central China. Among those brought to him were three small thrush-like birds with distinctive rust-coloured heads. Together with many other specimens brought back from the expedition these three birds were sent to the Rothschild Museum at Tring in Hertfordshire, where they were recognised by Ernst Hartert, one of the museum's bird experts, as being a species new to science, and were given the name *Luscinia ruficeps*. Later the three skins were transferred to the American Museum of Natural History. Nothing more was heard of the species until March 1963, when Elliott McClure, a scientist in charge of a United States Medical Research team, captured the fourth known specimen. This one was captured, however, not in central China, but near the summit of Mount Brinchang, a 6,600-foot peak in the central highlands of Malaya. In almost half a century between the two captures no other sightings of the rufous-headed thrush had been reported. Beyond the undoubted fact of its existence, nothing is known either of the present status of the species or of its distribution.

1948 was a great year of discovery in San Domingo, one rodent species being discovered for the first time and another being rediscovered after a lapse of well over a hundred years. In 1836 a new rodent species was discovered, described and named *Plagiodontia aedium*. After this nothing more was heard or seen of it until further specimens were discovered in 1948. The new species discovered at the same time was found to be a related species, which has been named *Plagiodontia hylaeum*.

At the time of writing the latest new mammal species to be discovered is a small wild cat, specimens of which were first captured in the Ryukya Islands, situated to the south of Japan, early in 1968. First reports describe the cats as being similar in appearance to the leopard cat, and it has been named *Mayailurus iriomotensis*. Two specimens are already on exhibition in a Japanese zoo.

The animals so far described in this chapter are species whose existence has been either confirmed or revealed for the first time in recent years. The total number of times any of them has been found is small. They must presumably be rare creatures, probably of limited distribution, and they have been seen by very few people.

One animal, however, for which there is only a single authentic record of sighting and capture, is nevertheless extremely well known all over the world because it has become a top favourite among pets. It is the golden hamster, *Mesocricetus auratus*. Until 1930 it was a completely unknown animal, but in that year Professor Ahorani discovered a female with a litter of twelve young in a burrow near Aleppo in Syria. He gathered them up and sent a few of them away to Europe for identification, where it was recognised that they were representatives of a hitherto unknown species of a group of rodents known as hamsters, a name derived from the German verb *hamstern*, meaning to hoard, and referring to the animal's habit of cramming their voluminous cheek pouches with food which they would afterwards eat at leisure. The offspring of the members of this litter were eventually distributed to many parts of Europe and America. Their potentialities as pets were soon discovered, and before long golden hamsters were being kept in almost every part of the world. The present population in captivity must number many millions, yet no more specimens have ever been found in the wild. But for one chance discovery the golden hamster—would still be an undiscovered and unsuspected species. This must be the most outstanding example of a species being saved from extinction by maintaining breeding stocks in captivity. It must be admitted, however, that its preservation was completely unpremeditated, being entirely due to its meteoric rise in popularity as a domestic pet.

The significant fact about all the animals so far described in this chapter is that any or all of them might still be unknown but for one or a few sightings or captures. Without these they would all still be animals whose existence remained unsuspected and which might at any time in the future be discovered. With this in mind it is quite impossible to maintain that there cannot be any more animals left to be discovered in the world, except for insects and other such small animals.

It must be admitted that all of these animals are quite small, and it is very likely that others of similar size may be discovered in the future. But what are the possibilities of the existence of considerably larger animals, either at present completely unsuspected, or the subject of unsubstantiated rumours? Before examining the evidence for the existence of a few of these, it might be as well to remind ourselves that even in the twentieth century several sizeable species have been discovered and made known to science for the first time, for example the okapi, discovered in central Africa in 1901; the giant forest hog, also discovered in central Africa in 1904; the mountain nyala, discovered in Abyssinia in 1908, and the golden takin, which was discovered in western China in 1919. In fact when one looks at the evidence dispassionately it seems likely that the animals still to be discovered must include at least a few larger species.

The possible existence of several of the potential future discoveries is already the subject of strong rumour, and to conclude this chapter we will examine the evidence for the existence of two species which have captured the popular imagination, the tiger cat of Australia and the yeti of the Himalayas. The Queensland tiger cat was first brought to scientific attention in 1871, when Mr P. L. Sclater, Secretary of the Zoological Society of

London, read to a meeting of the Society a letter he had received from Mr Brinsley Sheridan, Police Magistrate of Cardwell, in Queensland. This letter was in reply to one from Mr Sclater to Mr Sheridan following information he had received about Mr Sheridan's son having been attacked by a strange animal.

'I fear you must have misunderstood about my son having been attacked by some unknown ferocious animal in the bush. It was simply this. One evening, strolling along a path close to the shore of Rockingham Bay, a small terrier, my son's companion, took a scent up from a piece of scrub near the beach, and followed, barking furiously, towards the coast-range westwards. My boy (thirteen years of age, but an old bushman, who would put half those described in novels to the blush) followed and found in the long grass, about half a mile from the spot the scent was first taken up, an animal described by himself as follows: "It was lying camped in the long grass and was as big as a native Dog; its face was round like that of a Cat, it had a long tail, and its body was striped from the ribs under the belly with yellow and black. My Dog flew at it, but it could throw him. When they were together I fired my pistol at its head; the blood came. The animal then ran up a leaning tree, and the Dog barked at it. It then got savage and rushed down the tree at the Dog and then at me. I got frightened and came home".

'It was just dark when the boy came home in a high state of excitement and told me the story. From inquiry I find that this is not the first time a similar animal has been seen in this neighbourhood. Tracks of a sort of Tiger have been seen in Dalrymple's Gap by people camping there, and Mr Reginald Uhr, now Police Magistrate at St George, whilst one of the native mounted police officers in this district, saw the same animal my son described. The country is so sparsely populated, and the jungles (or, as we call them here "scrubs") so dense and so little known, that I have no doubt that animals of this kind exist in considerable numbers, the abundance of food and their timidity preventing our more intimate knowledge of their habits. I shall be most happy to send you, should it be my good fortune to drop across one of them, its skin and skeleton. I only regretted, as my poor boy did, that he had not my revolver, as he says he stood, when it was fighting with the Dog, at less than a yard from the animal.'

On receiving this letter Mr Sclater wrote to Mr Walter T. Scott, a Corresponding Member of the Zoological Society, who also lived at Cardwell, asking his opinion of Mr Sheridan's letter. In reply Mr Scott wrote: 'As to the Tiger, I am inclined to think there really is some large carnivorous animal as yet undescribed in this neighbourhood. A Mr Hull, Licensed Surveyor, was lately at work with a party of five men, surveying on the Murray and Mackay rivers, north of Cardwell. They were lying in their tents one night between eight and nine o'clock when they were all startled by a loud roar close to the tents. They seized their guns and carefully reconnoitred; but the animal had departed. In the morning they found the tracks of the unknown visitor, of which Mr Hull took the measurements and a rough sketch. I send you part of a leaf of Mr Hull's notebook, containing the original sketch—and also his drawing of the track, of the natural size. Mr Hull assures me that the drawing was a very faithful one, the soft ground having taken the impression with all its details. I have also examined some of the men who were with Mr Hull. They all tell the same story, and say they heard the animal three nights in succession.

'I think that I have already mentioned to you that a bullock-driver of ours, as long ago as 1864, came in one day with a story that he had seen a Tiger, but as he was a notorious liar we did not believe a word of it at the time. Yet it is possible he may have seen the same animal.'

From the same period there are other accounts of the mysterious tiger cat of Queensland, but none has ever been shot or captured, and so it remains one of the intriguing mysteries of the animal kingdom.

If we compare the marsupial or pouched mammals of Australia with the more advanced placental mammals found in other continents we find that the marsupials have developed types parallel in the modes of life to their placental counterparts. There are for example grazing, browsing, arboreal and burrowing types in both groups. The placental mammals have also developed large flesh-eating carnivores in each major continent. Asia has its tigers, lions and leopards; Africa its lions and leopards; and America its jaguars and pumas. One would therefore expect that the Australian marsupial fauna would also contain a parallel cat-like species. None is known, however, even from fossil records, so the hitherto unsuspected occurrence of an Australian tiger cat would certainly fit in with theoretical expectation.

Perhaps the best known of all the world's mystery animals is the yeti, or abominable snowman, the large creature reputed to live in the Himalayas. Although there are no completely authentic records of its having been seen, it is certainly believed in by the native Sherpas and others, and many of the best known western mountaineers who have climbed in the area have both seen and photographed its footprints. Such footprints were first reported in Europe by a mountaineer who was climbing on Everest's near neighbour Kanchenjunga in 1899. He reported a trail of very large footprints leading up the side of the mountain, and later climbers on Everest have found similar footprints in the soft snow as high as 20,000 feet.

Great mountaineers, who are conditioned to facing harsh reality, are hardly the kind of people to fall for fanciful myths, so it is extremely relevant to any consideration of the yeti to examine the experiences of the various Himalayan expeditions of the past few decades. In his 1936 Himalayan survey Eric Shipton reported seeing large footprints at about 16,000 feet. When he led the British Himalayan Expedition in 1951 he not only again saw similar footprints, which he followed for more than a mile, but was able to bring back excellent photographs of them taken at a height of about 19,000 feet.

His Sherpa guide, Sen Tensing, assured him that they were the footprints of the yeti. 'He told me' wrote Shipton in the *Geographical Journal* for June, 1952 'that two years before he and a number of other Sherpas had seen one of them at a distance of about twenty-five yards at Thyangboche. He described it as half man and half beast, standing about five feet six inches, with a tall pointed head, its body covered with reddish brown hair but with a hairless face.

'When we reached Katmundu at the end of November I had him cross-examined in Nepali (I conversed with him in Hindustani). He left no doubt as to his sincerity. Whatever it was that he had seen he was convinced that it was neither a bear nor a monkey, with both of which animals he was, of course, very familiar.'

The 1952 Swiss Everest Expedition also saw similar footprints at a height of about 16,500 feet. They described the prints as showing the marks of five toes of which only three apparently had claws.

1953 was of course the year of the successful ascent of Everest. In his account of this expedition which he led Sir John Hunt reports on a visit he made to the Abbot of the monastery at Thyangboche, who he questioned about the existence of the yeti. 'The old dignitary at once warmed to this subject. Peering out of the window on to the meadow where our tents were pitched, he gave a most graphic description of how a yeti had appeared from the surrounding thickets a few years back in winter, when the snow lay on the ground.

'This beast, loping along sometimes on his hind legs and sometimes on all fours, stood about five feet high and was covered with grey hair, a description which we have heard from other eyewitnesses. Oblivious of his guests, the Abbot was reliving a sight imprinted on his memory as he stared across at the scene of this event.'

As a result of all the accumulated evidence of the previous few years as to the existence of the yeti, the *Daily Mail* organised in 1954 a Snowman Expedition consisting of zoologists, climbers and a photographer, but although they spent nineteen weeks between 15,000 and 20,000 feet, no sighting of a snowman was achieved. At the same time they saw no snow leopards, or any evidence of their existence, yet these are known to be quite common in the area of the search.

Having summarised the evidence for the existence of the yeti, there remain several observations which must be made. The last expedition, with its considerable number of personnel and about thirty native porters, probably disturbed all the wild life in this normally almost completely isolated area for miles around, and ensured that even if any strange animals did exist they would keep well out of the way.

It has been suggested, too, that the yetis live in the many high uninhabited and virtually inaccessible valleys which abound among the Himalayan mountains, where they would have ample food and unlimited opportunity to keep themselves out of sight of anyone searching for them. Their appearance on the high snow slopes, according to this theory, only occurs when they are leaving one valley and crossing into another, sightings being extremely rare because the animal is mainly nocturnal, so that such journeys would usually be undertaken at night, when even the most enthusiastic expeditions are tucked away in their sleeping bags in such an inhospitable climate.

The Queensland tiger cat and the Himalayan yeti may or may not exist, and we can say the same about the various animals as yet undiscovered which are rumoured to live in the vast rain forests of tropical South America, or in the dense jungles of South Africa. For any of them the argument that if they really existed we should know about them is extremely weak. It is a fact that many animals whose existence is authenticated beyond any doubt have nevertheless been actually seen on only very rare occasions. Even today, nearly seventy years after it was made known to science by Sir Harry Johnstone, the okapi has still only been seen in its natural habitat by a handful of Europeans, despite the fact that throughout most of this period the country in which it lives has been under the rule of the Belgians. But for the almost fortuitous series of events which enabled him to supply the Zoological Society of London with the irrefutable evidence of the existence of this hitherto unknown species it might well still be today in the position of the tiger cat and the yeti—a species whose existence was based on nothing more than persistent native rumour.

The argument that an animal may well exist but yet prove almost impossible to find is certainly backed by the recent history of the thylacine or Tasmanian wolf, *Thylacinus cynocephalus*. This large carnivorous marsupial occupies the niche which is filled by the tigers, lions, leopards and jaguars in other parts of the world, and its counterpart, as we have already argued, should exist, or at least have existed in the past, on the Australian mainland. Of its existence there is no shadow of doubt, and this in a relatively small but well-wooded island. Even so David Fleay, one of Australia's leading naturalists reported in 1946 that although he had made several well organised attempts to locate and study it, he had been completely unsuccessful. The reason for his lack of success cannot have been that the animal had by this time become extinct, or at least no longer existed in the areas where he concentrated his searches, because in these areas fresh thylacine tracks were still quite common.

On balance, therefore, I think we must accept that there may well be quite a number of animal species, some of them of considerable size, still to be discovered and made known to science. Let us hope that when they are discovered the will to preserve them and the readiness of the prearranged preservation methods are both strong enough to give any such newly exposed species all the protection they need for survival, for they are almost certain to be rare, and probably also of more than usual scientific interest.

Index